Contents

Introduction

This book is designed for use as a flexible resource with Y6 students working towards level 4. It provides a wealth of practice – with and without a calculator – as well as offering teachers support in introducing the sheets. It deals with open number sentences in detail, breaks down aspects of solving word problems into manageable chunks and gives many contexts in which to practise extracting and using information.

It aims to address the implications of the QCA document 'Standards at Key Stage 2' and incorporate the needs of Y6 teachers and their students by utilizing the author's experience in the classroom and with Inset development.

'Standards at Key Stage 2' notes the following implications for teaching and learning:

- Children need practice in calculations involving conversion of metric units.

- Children need further experience of the inverse nature of the relationship between multiplication and division.

- Children need to develop better understanding of 'open' number sentences involving division, such as $527 \div \underline{\quad} = 31$, so that they come to appreciate that dividing by the 'answer' gives the missing term.

- Children need more opportunities to calculate with time so that their written and mental strategies acknowledge the base 60 nature of calculations for converting minutes to hours.

- Children should be encouraged to use calculators for questions that are difficult to do entirely mentally or where it is too inefficient to use a written method alone.

- Children should be given opportunities to explore the use of calculators in non-straightforward calculations such as calculations involving time, where time is rarely entered as a decimal.

- Further work is required to develop precision in children's understanding of mathematical vocabulary.

The book focuses on practice and reinforcement, it provides teachers with notes and OHTs to assist whole group learning and offers a number of copymasters for group and individual practice.

The book is written in four parts:-

Open number sentences: Students are required to manipulate sentences to find missing numbers with the emphasis on the inverse operation.

Word problems: The section is divided into manageable parts in which word problems are picked apart. Each part then focuses on one aspect of word problems.

Extracting information: Students are encouraged to generate their own questions based on the charts, graphs and information on the OHT. The level of questions asked can give the teacher insight into the level of mathematical confidence.

Test papers: Additional test papers have been included to test some of the principles studied in the scheme.

How to use this book

This book's simple structure enables teachers to adopt a flexible approach in using the resources. Written as a revision resource, the materials can be used at any time during years 5 or 6 for whole class numeracy lessons, as required.

The OHTs and teacher's notes can be used to generate class discussions or to target specific areas with small groups.

Each section contains five copymasters that are designed to provide progression and practice while building confidence and encouraging success. The first copymaster should be used with the class or group to open discussion; the second for individual practice; and the third for reinforcing the concept, assessment or as a homework activity.

Maths Boosters level 4 and 5 can be used to run parallel to each other for use with different levels of ability in a mixed ability classroom. Parts 1 and 2 follow the same topics to enable teachers to select the most suitable OHT. They can then differentiate using either level of copymaster.

This symbol denotes that the author recommends the use of a calculator for these activities.

Some students lack confidence in using calculators or use them indiscriminately, without thinking first. This book includes two copymasters in each section to encourage more efficient use of the calculator.

The transition from using paper and pencil methods to calculators can be difficult for some children and explanations need to be given and explored.

Students should always attempt to estimate the answer to a calculation before using the calculator. This helps them to check the answer and make sure that they have keyed in the correct figures. They should also use inverse operations, as appropriate, when checking their work.

Those tests that prohibit the use of calculators are signified with this symbol.

The tests include answer boxes for the students to do their working. They can then write their answers within the smaller box, as shown here.

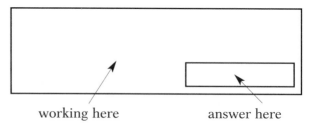

working here   answer here

___ + ___ = **20**

What two numbers could we write in here to make this sum correct?

Ask a student to suggest a pair of numbers. Write them in the spaces.

What other pairs of numbers could we use?

List some other pairs of numbers on the OHT.

Choose one of the pairs of numbers.

How can we use subtraction to check that this pair is correct?

20 − ___ = ___

Ask a student to explain how the method works. Repeat this using other pairs. Try repeating this activity with pairs that make 30 or 50 etc.

---

16 + ___ = **24**

Who can tell me the missing number? How did you work it out?

Did anyone use a different method to work out the missing number?

Discuss the methods suggested and try them out on other missing number sums.

Who can use subtraction to check the answer? How did you do it?

How are these next sums related to the first one?

Repeat this with **25** + ___ = **52** and other sums if you wish.

___ + ___ + **16** = **35**

Students need confidence in answering questions with more than one possible answer.

How can we do this one?

How much will the two missing numbers make together?

So what could they be?

Ask students to suggest numbers and explain how they worked it out.

Repeat the activity with other numbers.

___ + ___ + ___ = **54** can be used as a plenary activity.

What if the first number was 18?

Missing numbers: *addition*

___ + ___ = 20

20 − ___ = ___

16 + ___ = 24   24 − 16 = ___

___ + 16 = 24   24 − ___ = 16

25 + ___ = 52   52 − 25 = ___

___ + 25 = 52   52 − ___ = 25

___ + ___ + 16 = 35

___ + ___ + ___ = 54

Missing numbers: *addition*

Name _____

Fill in the missing number. Use subtraction to check your answer.

1. $12 + \_\_\_ = 19$ check $19 - 12 = \_\_\_$

2. $14 + \_\_\_ = 22$ check $22 - 14 = \_\_\_$

3. $23 + \_\_\_ = 31$ check $31 - 23 = \_\_\_$

4. $\_\_\_ + 27 = 42$ check $42 - 27 = \_\_\_$

5. $\_\_\_ + 34 = 51$ check _____

6. $\_\_\_ + 29 = 45$ check _____

7. $\_\_\_ + 19 = 33$ check _____

8. $\_\_\_ + 25 = 41$ check _____

9. $26 + \_\_\_ = 52$ check _____

10. $38 + \_\_\_ = 64$ check _____

Find three different pairs of numbers to complete each sum.

11. $\_\_\_ + 15 + \_\_\_ = 30$ 12. $\_\_\_ + 27 + \_\_\_ = 51$

$\_\_\_ + 15 + \_\_\_ = 30$ $\_\_\_ + 27 + \_\_\_ = 51$

$\_\_\_ + 15 + \_\_\_ = 30$ $\_\_\_ + 27 + \_\_\_ = 51$

13. $\_\_\_ + \_\_\_ + 18 = 37$ 14. $\_\_\_ + \_\_\_ + 26 = 64$

$\_\_\_ + \_\_\_ + 18 = 37$ $\_\_\_ + \_\_\_ + 26 = 64$

$\_\_\_ + \_\_\_ + 18 = 37$ $\_\_\_ + \_\_\_ + 26 = 64$

Missing numbers: *addition*

Name _____

Fill in the missing number. Use subtraction to check your answer.

1. $13 + \_\_\_ = 18$ check $18 - 13 = \_\_\_$

2. $16 + \_\_\_ = 33$ check $33 - 16 = \_\_\_$

3. $33 + \_\_\_ = 56$ check $56 - 33 = \_\_\_$

4. $\_\_\_ + 37 = 63$ check $63 - 37 = \_\_\_$

5. $\_\_\_ + 46 = 71$ check _____

6. $\_\_\_ + 39 = 64$ check _____

7. $\_\_\_ + 17 = 34$ check _____

8. $\_\_\_ + 35 = 61$ check _____

9. $36 + \_\_\_ = 53$ check _____

10. $49 + \_\_\_ = 66$ check _____

Find three different pairs of numbers to complete each sum.

11. $\_\_\_ + 17 + \_\_\_ = 36$ 12. $\_\_\_ + 37 + \_\_\_ = 56$

   $\_\_\_ + 17 + \_\_\_ = 36$ $\_\_\_ + 37 + \_\_\_ = 56$

   $\_\_\_ + 17 + \_\_\_ = 36$ $\_\_\_ + 37 + \_\_\_ = 56$

13. $\_\_\_ + \_\_\_ + 19 = 47$ 14. $\_\_\_ + \_\_\_ + 36 = 63$

   $\_\_\_ + \_\_\_ + 19 = 47$ $\_\_\_ + \_\_\_ + 36 = 63$

   $\_\_\_ + \_\_\_ + 19 = 47$ $\_\_\_ + \_\_\_ + 36 = 63$

Missing numbers: *addition*

Name _____

Fill in the missing number. Use subtraction to check your answer.

1. $14 + \underline{} = 25$ check $25 - 14 = \underline{}$

2. $17 + \underline{} = 31$ check $31 - 17 = \underline{}$

3. $23 + \underline{} = 45$ check $45 - 23 = \underline{}$

4. $\underline{} + 38 = 53$ check $53 - 38 = \underline{}$

5. $\underline{} + 45 = 81$ check _____

6. $\underline{} + 39 = 54$ check _____

7. $\underline{} + 18 = 34$ check _____

8. $\underline{} + 24 = 51$ check _____

9. $35 + \underline{} = 73$ check _____

10. $49 + \underline{} = 85$ check _____

Find three different pairs of numbers to complete each sum.

11. $\underline{} + 14 + \underline{} = 33$ 12. $\underline{} + 29 + \underline{} = 62$

$\underline{} + 14 + \underline{} = 33$ $\underline{} + 29 + \underline{} = 62$

$\underline{} + 14 + \underline{} = 33$ $\underline{} + 29 + \underline{} = 62$

13. $\underline{} + \underline{} + 23 = 45$ 14. $\underline{} + \underline{} + 38 = 73$

$\underline{} + \underline{} + 23 = 45$ $\underline{} + \underline{} + 38 = 73$

$\underline{} + \underline{} + 23 = 45$ $\underline{} + \underline{} + 38 = 73$

Missing numbers: *addition*

Name _____

Fill in the missing number. Use subtraction to check your answer.

1. 124 + ___ = 225   check 225 − 124 = ___

2. 134 + ___ = 341   check 341 − 134 = ___

3. 234 + ___ = 415   check 415 − 234 = ___

4. ___ + 138 = 153   check 153 − 138 = ___

5. ___ + 148 = 286   check _____

6. ___ + 319 = 534   check _____

7. ___ + 178 = 394   check _____

8. ___ + 214 = 571   check _____

9. 325 + ___ = 723   check _____

10. 419 + ___ = 875   check _____

Find three different pairs of numbers to complete each sum.

11. ___ + 124 + ___ = 313   12. ___ + 219 + ___ = 632

___ + 124 + ___ = 313   ___ + 219 + ___ = 632

___ + 124 + ___ = 313   ___ + 219 + ___ = 632

13. ___ + ___ + 232 = 456   14. ___ + ___ + 348 = 736

___ + ___ + 232 = 456   ___ + ___ + 348 = 736

___ + ___ + 232 = 456   ___ + ___ + 348 = 736

Missing numbers: *addition*

Name

Fill in the missing number. Use subtraction to check your answer.

1. $135 + \_\_\_ = 243$ check $243 - 135 = \_\_\_$

2. $147 + \_\_\_ = 358$ check $358 - 147 = \_\_\_$

3. $261 + \_\_\_ = 438$ check $438 - 261 = \_\_\_$

4. $\_\_\_ + 144 = 179$ check $179 - 144 = \_\_\_$

5. $\_\_\_ + 186 = 375$ check _____

6. $\_\_\_ + 349 = 588$ check _____

7. $\_\_\_ + 469 = 882$ check _____

8. $\_\_\_ + 337 = 856$ check _____

9. $348 + \_\_\_ = 785$ check _____

10. $1326 + \_\_\_\_ = 2842$ check _____

Find three different pairs of numbers to complete each sum. Use only three digit numbers.

11. $\_\_\_ + 234 + \_\_\_ = 447$ 12. $\_\_\_ + 354 + \_\_\_ = 717$

   $\_\_\_ + 234 + \_\_\_ = 447$ $\_\_\_ + 354 + \_\_\_ = 717$

   $\_\_\_ + 234 + \_\_\_ = 447$ $\_\_\_ + 354 + \_\_\_ = 717$

13. $\_\_\_ + \_\_\_ + 467 = 864$ 14. $\_\_\_ + \_\_\_ + 743 = 1435$

   $\_\_\_ + \_\_\_ + 467 = 864$ $\_\_\_ + \_\_\_ + 743 = 1435$

   $\_\_\_ + \_\_\_ + 467 = 864$ $\_\_\_ + \_\_\_ + 743 = 1435$

64 – ___ = 38

Uncover just the first subtraction problem. Ask the students how they would work it out. Reveal the number line. Choose a student to count on to find the missing number. Discuss ways of counting on. Draw the steps on the line as the students describe them.

We could add 2 first to make 40, then count in tens up to 60, then add the 4.
We could count in tens up to 58 and then count on in ones to 64.
How else can we say the calculation?

Encourage the use of different vocabulary. Lead the students to realise that the missing number can also be found by subtracting 38 from 64. You may need to illustrate this with simpler numbers for some students.

---

172 – ___ = 45

Do this calculation in the same way.

How can we check that our answer is correct?

Use addition to check both calculations. Ask the students to practise setting up a number line and using it to find more missing numbers. Then get them to convert the calculation so the answer is found by subtraction. Make sure that they check each one using addition.

___ – 27 = 52

(Finding the starting number of a subtraction calculation causes problems for many students and will need practise.) You may need to model the calculation on the OHT with easier numbers.

What if it was ___ – 4 = 5?

I have some cubes in my hand. When I give away 4 I still have 5 left. How many did I have to start with?
Do we expect the missing number to be more or less than 27? More or less than 52?

Show the students the number line. Choose a student to use it to find the missing number. Discuss the operation that you are using to solve a subtraction calculation.

___ – 36 = 129

Do this calculation in the same way. Show how the addition sum solves the problem. Practise some similar missing number calculations.

Missing numbers: *subtraction*

$$64 - \underline{} = 38$$

38   64

$$172 - \underline{} = 45$$

$$\begin{array}{r} 172 \\ -\ 45 \\ \hline \end{array}$$

45   172

$$\underline{} - 27 = 52$$

52   ___

$$\underline{} - 36 = 129$$

$$\begin{array}{r} 129 \\ +\ 36 \\ \hline \end{array}$$

129   ___

Missing numbers: *subtraction*

Name

Use the number line to fill in the missing numbers. Use addition to check your answers.

1. 17 _____ 35

   $35 - \underline{} = 17$ check $17 + \underline{} = 35$

2. 24 _____ 51

   $51 - \underline{} = 24$ check $24 + \underline{} = \underline{}$

3. 28 _____

   $163 - \underline{} = 28$ check $28 + \underline{} = \underline{}$

4. 75 _____

   $132 - \underline{} = 75$ check $\underline{} + \underline{} = \underline{}$

5. 122 _____

   $\underline{} - 57 = 122$ check $57 + 122 = \underline{}$

6. 84 _____

   $\underline{} - 29 = 84$ check $\underline{} + \underline{} = \underline{}$

Use addition or subtraction to solve these problems.

7. $\underline{} - 97 = 123$

8. $73 - \underline{} = 38$

9. $\underline{} - 67 = 85$

10. $145 - \underline{} = 88$

Missing numbers: *subtraction*

Name _____

Use the number line to fill in the missing numbers. Use addition to check your answers.

1. 15   32

    $32 - \underline{} = 15$ check $15 + \underline{} = 32$

2. 26   112

    $112 - \underline{} = 26$ check $26 + \underline{} = \underline{}$

3. 29

    $85 - \underline{} = 29$ check $\underline{} + \underline{} = \underline{}$

4. 54

    $141 - \underline{} = 54$ check $\underline{} + \underline{} = \underline{}$

5. 18

    $\underline{} - 56 = 18$ check $56 + 18 = \underline{}$

6. 69

    $\underline{} - 32 = 69$ check $69 + \underline{} = \underline{}$

Use addition or subtraction to solve these problems.

7. $\underline{} - 137 = 85$

8. $87 - \underline{} = 59$

9. $\underline{} - 64 = 93$

10. $145 - \underline{} = 96$

Missing numbers: *subtraction*

Name _____

Use the number line to fill in the missing numbers. Use addition to check
your answers.

1. $\overline{21 \qquad\qquad\qquad 36}$

    $36 - \underline{\quad} = 21$ check $21 + \underline{\quad} = 36$

2. $\overline{23 \qquad\qquad\qquad\quad}$

    $62 - \underline{\quad} = 23$ check $23 + \underline{\quad} = 62$

3. $\overline{78 \qquad\qquad\qquad\quad}$

    $147 - \underline{\quad} = 78$ check $\underline{\quad} + \underline{\quad} = \underline{\quad}$

4. $\overline{87 \qquad\qquad\qquad\quad}$

    $164 - \underline{\quad} = 87$ check $\underline{\quad} + \underline{\quad} = \underline{\quad}$

5. $\overline{26 \qquad\qquad\qquad\quad}$

    $\underline{\quad} - 19 = 26$ check $19 + 26 = \underline{\quad}$

6. $\overline{137 \qquad\qquad\qquad\quad}$

    $\underline{\quad} - 28 = 137$ check $137 + \underline{\quad} = \underline{\quad}$

Use addition or subtraction to solve these calculations.

7. $\underline{\quad} - 67 = 146$

8. $\underline{\quad} - 68 = 114$

9. $162 - \underline{\quad} = 118$

10. $\underline{\quad} - 82 = 157$

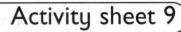

Missing numbers: *subtraction*

Name _____

Find the missing numbers. Record your working.

1. $265 - \underline{\ \ \ } = 195$

2. $\underline{\ \ \ } - 344 = 612$

3. $1056 - \underline{\ \ \ } = 339$

4. $766 - \underline{\ \ \ } = 318$

5. $\underline{\ \ \ } - 541 = 498$

6. $1354 - \underline{\ \ \ } = 94$

7. $\underline{\ \ \ } - 75 = 482$

8. $738 - \underline{\ \ \ } = 276$

9. $1854 - \underline{\ \ \ } = 127$

10. $\underline{\ \ \ } - 633 = 1280$

Find the missing numbers. There is more than one possible answer. Record all your working.

11. $350 - \underline{\ \ \ } - \underline{\ \ \ } = 220$

12. $550 - \underline{\ \ \ } - \underline{\ \ \ } = 300$

13. $\underline{\ \ \ } - 75 - 120 = 105$

14. $950 - \underline{\ \ \ } - \underline{\ \ \ } = 620$

15. $\underline{\ \ \ } - 80 - 225 = 195$

Missing numbers: *subtraction*

Name _____

Find the missing numbers. Record all your working.

1. ___ − 84 = 129

2. ___ − 58 = 227

3. 563 − ___ = 224

4. ___ − 194 = 168

5. 1071 − ___ = 664

6. ___ − 819 = 337

7. 495 − ___ = 206

8. 8788 − ___ = 394

9. ___ − 567 = 3299

10. ___ − 786 = 12 934

Find the missing numbers. There is more than one possible answer. Record all your working.

11. 440 − ___ − ___ = 180

12. 1040 − ___ − ___ = 550

13. ___ − 85 − 320 = 125

14. 860 − ___ − ___ = 250

15. ___ − 90 − 305 = 290

__ × __ = 36

What two numbers could we write in here to make this calculation correct?

Ask a student to suggest a pair of numbers and write them on the OHT.

What other pairs of numbers could we use?

List other pairs of numbers on the OHT. Choose one of the pairs of numbers.

How can we use division to check that this pair is correct?

36 ÷ __ = __

Choose a student to explain the method. Repeat this for other pairs. Now choose another number, e.g. 30 or 42, and get the students to give you pairs of factors. Use division to check the answer.

---

6 × ___ = 24

Who can tell me the missing number? How did you work it out?
Did anyone use a different method to work out the missing number?

Discuss the methods suggested. Practise using division to find the missing number. Do the same for the other calculations on the OHT. Always multiply the missing number to check the answer.

---

7 × __ = 105

How can we do this one?
It is unlikely that you know your seven times table up to 105 so what method can we use to find the missing number?

Do the division calculation together and check it using multiplication.

Repeat the activity with __ × 9 = 135

Practise solving other missing multiplication number calculations by using division.

Missing numbers:
multiplication

___ × ___ = 36

36 ÷ ___ = ___

6 × ___ = 24   24 ÷ 6 = ___

___ × 8 = 56   56 ÷ 8 = ___

___ × 7 = 63   63 ÷ 7 = ___

7 × ___ = 105   105 ÷ 7 = ___

7)105   check   □
                      × 7

___ × 9 = 135   135 ÷ 9 = ___

9)135   check   □
                      × 9

Missing numbers:
multiplication

Name

Use division to find the missing number.

1. $4 \times \underline{\quad} = 28$ $28 \div 4 = \underline{\quad}$

2. $\underline{\quad} \times 6 = 36$ $36 \div 6 = \underline{\quad}$

3. $9 \times \underline{\quad} = 45$ $45 \div 9 = \underline{\quad}$

4. $8 \times \underline{\quad} = 64$ $64 \div 8 = \underline{\quad}$

5. $\underline{\quad} \times 7 = 42$ $42 \div 7 = \underline{\quad}$

6. $9 \times \underline{\quad} = 81$ $81 \div 9 = \underline{\quad}$

7. $8 \times \underline{\quad} = 72$ $72 \div 8 = \underline{\quad}$

8. $4 \times \underline{\quad} = 36$ $36 \div 4 = \underline{\quad}$

9. $\underline{\quad} \times 6 = 54$ $54 \div 6 = \underline{\quad}$

10. $9 \times \underline{\quad} = 63$ $63 \div 9 = \underline{\quad}$

Now try these. Check your answers using multiplication.

11. $9 \times \underline{\quad} = 153$ $9\overline{)153}$ $\boxed{}$
                        $\times \quad 9$

12. $8 \times \underline{\quad} = 136$ $8\overline{)136}$ $\boxed{}$
                        $\times \quad 8$

13. $6 \times \underline{\quad} = 156$

14. $\underline{\quad} \times 4 = 144$

15. $7 \times \underline{\quad} = 133$

Missing numbers:
multiplication

Name _____

Use division to find the missing number.

1. ___ × 3 = 27   27 ÷ 3 = ___

2. 6 × ___ = 42   42 ÷ 6 = ___

3. 9 × ___ = 36   36 ÷ 9 = ___

4. ___ × 8 = 80   80 ÷ 8 = ___

5. 4 × ___ = 32   32 ÷ 4 = ___

6. ___ × 9 = 72   72 ÷ 9 = ___

7. 8 × ___ = 48   48 ÷ 8 = ___

8. 3 × ___ = 24   24 ÷ 3 = ___

9. 5 × ___ = 45   45 ÷ 5 = ___

10. ___ × 7 = 63   63 ÷ 7 = ___

Now try these. Check your answers using multiplication.

11. 7 × ___ = 154 $7\overline{)154}$ □
                                        ×   7

12. ___ × 6 = 138 $6\overline{)138}$ □
                                        ×   6

13. 8 × ___ = 176

14. 4 × ___ = 156

15. ___ × 9 = 162

Missing numbers:
multiplication

Name

Use division to find the missing number.

1. $5 \times \underline{\hspace{1cm}} = 35$ $35 \div 5 = \underline{\hspace{1cm}}$

2. $\underline{\hspace{1cm}} \times 6 = 48$ $48 \div 6 = \underline{\hspace{1cm}}$

3. $\underline{\hspace{1cm}} \times 9 = 54$ $54 \div 9 = \underline{\hspace{1cm}}$

4. $8 \times \underline{\hspace{1cm}} = 56$ $56 \div 8 = \underline{\hspace{1cm}}$

5. $3 \times \underline{\hspace{1cm}} = 21$ $21 \div 3 = \underline{\hspace{1cm}}$

6. $7 \times \underline{\hspace{1cm}} = 49$ $49 \div 7 = \underline{\hspace{1cm}}$

7. $\underline{\hspace{1cm}} \times 8 = 32$ $32 \div 8 = \underline{\hspace{1cm}}$

8. $7 \times \underline{\hspace{1cm}} = 28$ $28 \div 7 = \underline{\hspace{1cm}}$

9. $8 \times \underline{\hspace{1cm}} = 40$ $40 \div 8 = \underline{\hspace{1cm}}$

10. $\underline{\hspace{1cm}} \times 7 = 56$ $56 \div 7 = \underline{\hspace{1cm}}$

Now try these. Check your answers using multiplication.

11. $\underline{\hspace{1cm}} \times 4 = 172$ $4\overline{)172}$ $\boxed{}$
$$\times \quad 4$$

12. $6 \times \underline{\hspace{1cm}} = 252$ $6\overline{)252}$ $\boxed{}$
$$\times \quad 6$$

13. $\underline{\hspace{1cm}} \times 9 = 243$

14. $7 \times \underline{\hspace{1cm}} = 238$

15. $8 \times \underline{\hspace{1cm}} = 192$

Missing numbers:
multiplication

Name

Find the missing number. Record your working.

1. $13 \times \underline{\quad} = 182$

2. $\underline{\quad} \times 15 = 285$

3. $14 \times \underline{\quad} = 252$

4. $\underline{\quad} \times 23 = 437$

5. $\underline{\quad} \times 19 = 323$

6. $17 \times \underline{\quad} = 272$

7. $16 \times \underline{\quad} = 288$

8. $24 \times \underline{\quad} = 312$

9. $\underline{\quad} \times 18 = 342$

10. $\underline{\quad} \times 26 = 364$

Find the missing numbers. Both numbers are less than 25. Record your working.

11. $\underline{\quad} \times \underline{\quad} = 126$

12. $\underline{\quad} \times \underline{\quad} = 114$

13. $\underline{\quad} \times \underline{\quad} = 143$

14. $\underline{\quad} \times \underline{\quad} = 136$

15. $\underline{\quad} \times \underline{\quad} = 162$

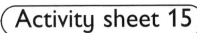

Missing numbers:
multiplication

Name _____

Find the missing number. Record your working.

1. $14 \times \underline{} = 238$

2. $\underline{} \times 15 = 270$

3. $17 \times \underline{} = 357$

4. $\underline{} \times 25 = 425$

5. $\underline{} \times 13 = 286$

6. $15 \times \underline{} = 240$

7. $26 \times \underline{} = 364$

8. $21 \times \underline{} = 462$

9. $\underline{} \times 13 = 338$

10. $\underline{} \times 23 = 437$

Find the missing numbers so that all three numbers are more than 2 and less than 15. Record your working.

11. $\underline{} \times \underline{} \times \underline{} = 60$

12. $\underline{} \times \underline{} \times \underline{} = 90$

13. $\underline{} \times \underline{} \times \underline{} = 105$

14. $\underline{} \times \underline{} \times \underline{} = 96$

15. $\underline{} \times \underline{} \times \underline{} = 135$

24 ÷ ___ = ___

What two numbers could we use to make this calculation correct?

Ask a student to suggest a pair of numbers. Write them in the spaces.

What other pairs of numbers could we use?

List other pairs of numbers on the OHT. Choose one of the pairs of numbers

---

How can we use multiplication to check that this pair is correct?

___ × ___ = 24

Choose a student to explain the method. Repeat this for other pairs. Now choose another number, e.g. 36 or 40, and get the students to suggest pairs of factors. Use multiplication to check.

---

42 ÷ ___ = 6

How can we work out the missing number? What do we know about division that will help us? Who can tell me the missing number? How did you work it out? Did anyone use a different method to work out the missing number?

Discuss the methods suggested and practise using division to find the missing number. Do the same for the other calculations on the OHT. Multiply the missing number to check the answer.
You may need to do some revision of short division before the next part.

---

96 ÷ ___ = 6

How can we do this one? It is unlikely that you know your six times table up to 96 so what method can we use to find the missing number?

Do the division calculation together then check it using multiplication.

Repeat the activity with **144 ÷ ___ = 9**

Practise solving other missing number division calculations in this way.

You may want to leave the next part of the OHT to another session as it deals with a different missing element.

___ ÷ 5 = 8

How can we work out the missing number? What do we know about division that will help us? Who can tell me the missing number? How did you work it out?
Practise with other missing numbers.

Missing numbers: *division*

24 ÷ ___ = ___

___ × ___ = 24

42 ÷ ___ = 6	42 ÷ 6 = ___	6 × ___ = 42
32 ÷ ___ = 8	32 ÷ 8 = ___	8 × ___ = 32
35 ÷ ___ = 7	35 ÷ 7 = ___	7 × ___ = 35

96 ÷ ___ = 6   6)96

144 ÷ ___ = 9   9)144

___ ÷ 5 = 8   8 × 5 = ___

___ ÷ 4 = 7   4 × 7 = ___

___ ÷ 15 = 9   15 × 9 = ___

Missing numbers: *division*

Name

Fill in the missing numbers.

1. $27 \div \underline{} = 3$ $27 \div 3 = \underline{}$ $3 \times \underline{} = 27$

2. $32 \div \underline{} = 8$ $32 \div 8 = \underline{}$ $8 \times \underline{} = 32$

3. $45 \div \underline{} = 5$ $45 \div 5 = \underline{}$ $5 \times \underline{} = 45$

4. $24 \div \underline{} = 4$ $24 \div 4 = \underline{}$ $4 \times \underline{} = 24$

5. $42 \div \underline{} = 6$ $42 \div 6 = \underline{}$ $6 \times \underline{} = 42$

6. $40 \div \underline{} = 8$ $40 \div 8 = \underline{}$ $8 \times \underline{} = 40$

Show your working for these calculations.

7. $96 \div \underline{} = 4$

8. $84 \div \underline{} = 6$

9. $75 \div \underline{} = 3$

10. $112 \div \underline{} = 8$

Now try these.

11. $\underline{} \div 5 = 7$ $5 \times 7 = \underline{}$

12. $\underline{} \div 6 = 3$ $6 \times 3 = \underline{}$

13. $\underline{} \div 14 = 7$ $14 \times 7 = \underline{}$

14. $\underline{} \div 3 = 19$ $19 \times 3 = \underline{}$

15. $\underline{} \div 17 = 6$ $17 \times 6 = \underline{}$

Missing numbers: *division*

Name _____

Fill in the missing numbers.

1. $21 \div \underline{\quad} = 3$ $\qquad$ $21 \div 3 = \underline{\quad}$ $\qquad$ $3 \times \underline{\quad} = 21$

2. $36 \div \underline{\quad} = 4$ $\qquad$ $36 \div 4 = \underline{\quad}$ $\qquad$ $4 \times \underline{\quad} = 36$

3. $56 \div \underline{\quad} = 7$ $\qquad$ $56 \div 7 = \underline{\quad}$ $\qquad$ $7 \times \underline{\quad} = 56$

4. $35 \div \underline{\quad} = 5$ $\qquad$ $35 \div 5 = \underline{\quad}$ $\qquad$ $5 \times \underline{\quad} = 35$

5. $81 \div \underline{\quad} = 9$ $\qquad$ $81 \div 9 = \underline{\quad}$ $\qquad$ $9 \times \underline{\quad} = 81$

6. $54 \div \underline{\quad} = 6$ $\qquad$ $54 \div 6 = \underline{\quad}$ $\qquad$ $6 \times \underline{\quad} = 54$

Show your working for these calculations.

7. $91 \div \underline{\quad} = 7$

8. $135 \div \underline{\quad} = 9$

9. $138 \div \underline{\quad} = 6$

10. $136 \div \underline{\quad} = 8$

Now try these.

11. $\underline{\quad} \div 8 = 3$ $\qquad$ $8 \times 3 = \underline{\quad}$

12. $\underline{\quad} \div 7 = 4$ $\qquad$ $7 \times 4 = \underline{\quad}$

13. $\underline{\quad} \div 5 = 18$ $\qquad$ $5 \times 18 = \underline{\quad}$

14. $\underline{\quad} \div 9 = 14$ $\qquad$ $9 \times 14 = \underline{\quad}$

15. $\underline{\quad} \div 8 = 17$ $\qquad$ $8 \times 17 = \underline{\quad}$

Missing numbers: *division*

Name _____

Find the missing numbers.

1. 24 ÷ ___ = 3   24 ÷ 3 = ___   3 × ___ = 24

2. 32 ÷ ___ = 4   32 ÷ 4 = ___   4 × ___ = 32

3. 50 ÷ ___ = 5   50 ÷ 5 = ___   5 × ___ = 50

4. 48 ÷ ___ = 6   48 ÷ 6 = ___   6 × ___ = 48

5. 72 ÷ ___ = 9   72 ÷ 9 = ___   9 × ___ = 72

6. 49 ÷ ___ = 7   49 ÷ 7 = ___   7 × ___ = 49

Show your working for these calculations.

7. 162 ÷ ___ = 9

8. 144 ÷ ___ = 6

9. 189 ÷ ___ = 7

10. 171 ÷ ___ = 3

Now try these.

11. ___ ÷ 6 = 8   8 × 6 = ___

12. ___ ÷ 7 = 9   7 × 9 = ___

13. ___ ÷ 4 = 23   4 × 23 = ___

14. ___ ÷ 5 = 18   5 × 18 = ___

15. ___ ÷ 8 = 22   8 × 22 = ___

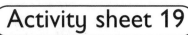

Missing numbers: *division*

Name _____

Find the missing numbers. Record all your working.

1. 256 ÷ ___ = 16

2. ___ ÷ 18 = 18

3. 273 ÷ ___ = 21

4. 285 ÷ ___ = 15

5. ___ ÷ 16 = 12

6. 396 ÷ ___ = 18

7. ___ ÷ 17 = 17

8. 361 ÷ ___ = 19

9. 308 ÷ ___ = 14

10. ___ ÷ 17 = 21

Find the missing numbers. Both numbers are two digit numbers less than 25.
Record all your working.

11. 272 ÷ ___ = ___

12. 462 ÷ ___ = ___

13. 399 ÷ ___ = ___

14. 414 ÷ ___ = ___

15. 323 ÷ ___ = ___

Missing numbers: *division*

Name

Find the missing numbers. Record all your working.

1. 391 ÷ ___ = 17

2. ___ ÷ 16 = 18

3. 432 ÷ ___ = 24

4. 456 ÷ ___ = 19

5. ___ ÷ 19 = 16

6. 304 ÷ ___ = 16

7. ___ ÷ 17 = 18

8. 475 ÷ ___ = 19

9. 399 ÷ ___ = 21

10. ___ ÷ 17 = 24

Find the missing numbers. Both numbers are two digit numbers less than 25.
Record all your working.

11. 432 ÷ ___ = ___

12. 437 ÷ ___ = ___

13. 336 ÷ ___ = ___

14. 418 ÷ ___ = ___

15. 247 ÷ ___ = ___

This section should be used as a final check. Employ all four operations to find the missing numbers.

___ + 59 = 133

Ask the students how they can find the missing number. Use a blank number line and see if a student can draw the sum. Ask the class if they can use subtraction to find the missing number. If this causes problems substitute easier numbers.

Can someone write a similar missing number sum for us to solve?

74 + ___ = 152

Look at the next sum on the OHT. Discuss whether a change in the position of the missing number will mean changing the approach to the solution. Check the answers.

Can someone write a similar missing number sum for us to solve?

113 – ___ = 76

Ask the students how they can find the missing number.
Can anyone draw the calculation on a blank number line?
Ask the students which operation they must use to find the missing number. If this causes problems substitute easier numbers.

Can someone write a similar missing number calculation for us to solve?

___ – 68 = 86

Look at the next calculation on the OHT. Discuss whether the change of position of the missing number means any change in approach to a solution. Ask the students to estimate the size of the missing number. Check the answer.

Can someone write a similar missing number calculation for us to solve?

___ × 5 = 95

Follow the same procedure for the other calculations on the OHT. Look at the position of the missing number and estimate the size of the answer to decide the method needed to find a solution.

___ + ___ + ___ = 125

This sum could be set as a challenge to small groups using different sets of parameters for the missing numbers e.g. all the numbers must be bigger than 35, no even numbers, one number greater than 80, and so on.

The students could set similar challenges for each other with or without restrictions.

___ × ___ × ___ = 126

This can be set as a challenge for the students.

Missing numbers: *mixed*

___ + 59 = 133

74 + ___ = 152

113 − ___ = 76

___ − 68 = 86

___ × 5 = 95   4 × ___ = 92

104 ÷ ___ = 8   ___ ÷ 6 = 108

___ + ___ + ___ = 125

___ × ___ × ___ = 126

Missing numbers: *mixed*

Name _____

Find the missing numbers. Show your working each time.

1. $56 + \underline{\quad} = 113$

2. $75 - \underline{\quad} = 29$

3. $\underline{\quad} + 77 = 132$

4. $5 \times \underline{\quad} = 45$

5. $\underline{\quad} \div 8 = 9$

6. $\underline{\quad} \times 6 = 36$

7. $114 - \underline{\quad} = 38$

8. $\underline{\quad} - 69 = 123$

9. $48 \div \underline{\quad} = 8$

10. $\underline{\quad} \times 9 = 63$

11. $182 \div \underline{\quad} = 7$

12. $\underline{\quad} \times 6 = 192$

13. $\underline{\quad} - 156 = 73$

14. $289 + \underline{\quad} = 466$

15. $\underline{\quad} \div 6 = 19$

16. $\underline{\quad} - 158 = 143$

Missing numbers: *mixed*

Name _____

Find the missing numbers. Show your working each time.

1. $6 \times$ ___ $= 48$

2. $86 -$ ___ $= 58$

3. ___ $+ 47 = 116$

4. $63 +$ ___ $= 142$

5. ___ $\div 9 = 7$

6. ___ $\times 8 = 32$

7. $235 -$ ___ $= 184$

8. $8 \times$ ___ $= 216$

9. $49 \div$ ___ $= 7$

10. ____ $- 148 = 161$

11. $208 \div$ ___ $= 4$

12. ___ $\times 7 = 196$

13. ___ $\times 9 = 135$

14. $191 +$ ____ $= 417$

15. ___ $\div 6 = 31$

16. ____ $- 245 = 172$

Missing numbers: *mixed*

Name

Find the missing numbers. Show your working each time.

1. ___ $\div 9 = 9$

2. $8 \times$ ___ $= 72$

3. ___ $+ 72 = 111$

4. $94 -$ ___ $= 38$

5. $75 +$ ___ $= 134$

6. ___ $\times 8 = 64$

7. ___ $\times 6 = 228$

8. $7 \times$ ___ $= 294$

9. $56 \div$ ___ $= 7$

10. ____ $- 269 = 194$

11. $215 \div$ ___ $= 5$

12. $162 -$ ___ $= 107$

13. ___ $- 237 = 266$

14. $278 +$ ____ $= 405$

15. ___ $\div 8 = 37$

16. ___ $\div 9 = 13$

Missing numbers: *mixed*

Name

Find the missing numbers. Show all your working each time.

1. $364 + \underline{\qquad} = 711$

2. $846 - \underline{\qquad} = 459$

3. $37 \times \underline{\qquad} = 1924$

4. $1620 \div \underline{\qquad} = 36$

5. $\underline{\qquad} + 2479 = 3022$

6. $\underline{\qquad} - 685 = 596$

7. $\underline{\qquad} \times 29 = 1044$

8. $\underline{\qquad} \div 28 = 42$

9. $1014 \div \underline{\qquad} = 26$

10. $\underline{\qquad} \times 23 = 1173$

Find the missing numbers. They are all 3 digit numbers.

11. $\underline{\qquad} + \underline{\qquad} = 274$

12. $\underline{\qquad} - \underline{\qquad} = 86$

13. $\underline{\qquad} + \underline{\qquad} = 317$

14. $\underline{\qquad} - \underline{\qquad} = 419$

15. $\underline{\qquad} - \underline{\qquad} = 307$

Missing numbers: *mixed*

Name _____

Find the missing numbers. Show all your working each time.

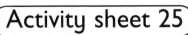

1. $285 + \underline{} = 518$

2. $1096 - \underline{} = 538$

3. $46 \times \underline{} = 1610$

4. $1484 \div \underline{} = 53$

5. $\underline{} + 1844 = 3996$

6. $\underline{} - 486 = 339$

7. $\underline{} \times 47 = 2397$

8. $\underline{} \div 24 = 63$

9. $1482 \div \underline{} = 39$

10. $\underline{} \times 33 = 2046$

All the missing numbers are greater than 2 and less than 15.

11. $\underline{} \times \underline{} \times \underline{} = 150$

12. $\underline{} \times \underline{} \times \underline{} = 162$

13. $\underline{} \times \underline{} \times \underline{} = 144$

The missing numbers are two digit numbers less than 25.

14. $216 \div \underline{} = \underline{}$

15. $247 \div \underline{} = \underline{}$

Brainstorm all the words to do with addition and subtraction. List them on the OHT.

Who can make up an addition problem using the word... ? (Choose one of the words previously suggested by the students.)
Repeat this for other addition vocabulary.

Who can make up a subtraction problem using the word... ? (Choose one of the words previously suggested by the students.)
Repeat this for other subtraction vocabulary.

What is the...
Look at the first two problems on the OHT. Identify the key words that tell us whether to add or subtract.

How many more...
Explain that the way the words are used can change the problem from an addition to a subtraction calculation. Look at the next two problems on the OHT. Discuss ways of solving them.

What are the key words that tell us whether to add or subtract?

Get students to underline key words.

How do we know whether to add or subtract?
What do you think the answer will be?
Do we expect the answer to be more or less than this number in the question? Why?

What is the total...
Repeat this method for other pairs of problems.

Get the students to use different vocabulary to make up their own problems.

Who can make up an addition problem using the word 'total'? e.g. What is the total cost...?
What is the total score...?
Who can make up a subtraction problem using the word 'total'? e.g. If the total is... how much...?

Ask some students to suggest problems and get some other students to work them out and check them.

Students could write their own pairs of problems using a variety of mathematical vocabulary and then swap sheets to work out each other's problems.

Solving problems: *vocabulary of add and subtract*

Addition	Subtraction

What is the total cost of a £3.55 book and a £5.60 game?

A bag of sweets weighs 975g and a bag of biscuits weighs 850g. How much less do the biscuits weigh?

Jo	Bill	Ann

25 stickers	36 stickers	19 stickers

How many more stickers does Bill have than Jo?
Ann collects 17 more stickers. How many does she have now?

What is the total of Ann and Jo's stickers?

If Bill wants a total of 54 stickers how many more must he collect?

What is the difference between Ann and Bill's stickers?

If the difference between Jo and Alex's stickers is 27 how many stickers does Alex have?

17/09/10

Solving problems: *vocabulary of add and subtract*

Name _____

1. Ray's baby pet snake is 17cm long and its mother is 42cm long. How much longer is the mother snake than the baby snake? _____

2. To go on holiday Gayan travelled 25 km by bus and 237 km by train. How far did he travel altogether? _____

3. A bus can carry 53 passengers. If there are already 27 passengers on board how many more can the bus carry? _____

4. A pen was 86p but the shop increased the price by 35p. How much does a pen cost after the increase? _____

5. Gwen played tiddlywinks and scored 134 in the first round and 172 in the second. What was her total score? _____

6. Sarah needed a piece of shelving 156cm long. The wood she bought was 240cm long. How much did she have left? _____

7. What is the difference in cost between pairs of Mike trainers for £32.50 and a pair of Bonnay trainers for £27.50? _____

8. When Eric first measured his sunflower it was 157cm tall. When he measured it again it had increased by 44cm. How tall was it?

   _____

9. Jack was making a cake and needed 275g of flour. He accidently poured in 320g. How much must he take out? _____

10. I have two jugs of milk. One holds 550ml the other holds 775ml. How much milk have I altogether? _____

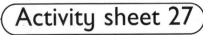

Solving problems: *vocabulary of add and subtract*

Name _____

1. A train travelled for 50 minutes to the first station and 45 minutes to the next station. How long had it been travelling? _____

2. Two puppies weigh 520g and 455g. What is the difference in their weights? _____

3. Meg bought a book for £4.75 and a CD for £6.50. What is the total cost? _____

4. Kym's book has 136 pages. He has read 97 pages. How many more pages has he left to read? _____

5. Last year 468 people came to the school play. This year there was an increase of 72. How many people came this year? _____

6. In a sale the price of a CD player was decreased by £99. Its original price was £449. What is the sale price? _____

7. When Yasmin played darts she scored 65, 83 and 34. What is the sum of her scores? _____

8. Due to road works Ally had to take the long way home. Her journey took 45 minutes longer than the usual 25 minutes. How long did her journey take? _____

9. How much cheaper is a Didas sweat shirt for £15.45 than a Renetton one for £22.99? _____

10. Bill wants to make his patio 36 slabs bigger. It already has an area of 56 slabs. What will the new total area be? _____

Solving problems: *vocabulary of add and subtract*

Name _____

1. John bought 125m of fencing but only needed 97m. How much did he have left? _____

2. Sam increased his stamp collection by 37 stamps to a total of 76 stamps. How many did he have before? _____

3. Danny had to write a story of at least 250 words. When he had written 185 words how many more did he need to write? _____

4. A car travels 135km and stops for petrol. It then travels 76km. How far has it travelled altogether? _____

5. In a cricket match Park School scored 124 runs. Meadow School scored 86 runs. What was the difference between their scores? _____

6. An aeroplane can carry 255 passengers. If 188 passengers board the plane, how many more passengers can board? _____

7. A pair of Bro trousers cost £25.90 and a Gatta shirt costs £16.49. What is the total cost of the two items? _____

8. Megan was going to put 175g of sugar in a cake but decided to increase the quantity by 150g. How much sugar did she use? _____

9. There were 265 parents at Sports Day last year. This year there were 197. By how many did the number of parents decrease? _____

10. Bethan gained 27 marks in one science test and 38 marks in another. What is the sum of her marks? _____

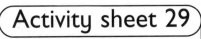
Solving problems: *vocabulary of add and subtract*

Name _____

1. What is the sum of 123, 45 and 376? _____

2. What is the difference between 1245km and 3654km?

    _____

3. Exeter to Oxford is 154 miles. Exeter to Aberdeen is 587

    miles. How much further is it from Exeter to Aberdeen than from

    Exeter to Oxford? _____

4. A postman has three parcels to deliver weighing 1·2kg, 1·25kg and

    1·5kg. What is the total weight of the parcels? _____

5. At a football match last week there were 15 765 fans. This week there

    were 1344 fewer fans. How many fans attended this week? _____

6. Eric earns £15.85 a week on his paper round. His brother, James, earns

    £17.50 washing cars. How much more than Eric does James earn?

    _____

7. Mr. Evans sells his house for £97 800. He buys his new house for

    £111 250. How much more is the new house? _____

8. A secondhand car leaves the garage with 47 998 miles on the clock.

    After 3 months this has increased by 6750 miles. What is the new

    reading on the clock? _____

9. A house has been on the market for a long time at a price of £110 950.

    The owners decide to decrease the price by £15 500. What is the new

    price? _____

10. British Airflights Company carried 25 600 passengers in January, 23 550

    in February and 28 750 in March. What is the total number of

    passengers for the three months? _____

1. At a pop concert last week there were 35 990 fans. This week that number decreased by 2885. How many attended this week? _____

2. What is the difference between 10 087 and 346?

    _____

3. The diameter of Earth is 12 756 km and the diameter of Mars is 6800km. How much more is the diameter of Earth than the diameter of Mars?

    _____

4. A dog breeder has three new puppies weighing 1·35 kg, 0·75kg and 1·4kg. What is the total weight of the puppies? _____

5. What is the sum of £3.67, £4.90 and 37p? _____

6. The area of the United Kingdom is 244 880 square km. The area of France is 551 500 square km. How much smaller is the United Kingdom than France? _____

7. The longest river is the Nile at 6695km. How much longer is it than the River Congo at 4667km? _____

8. A business tycoon makes £350 000 profit on a deal. The deal continues to make money and increases by £95 850. How much profit does he make altogether? _____

9. Cross Channel Ferries carried 85 650 passengers in July, 91 445 in August and 72 886 in September. What is the total number of passengers for the three months? _____

10. A charity needs to raise £1 450 000 for a major project. They raise £860 000 in three months. How much more do they need? _____

Brainstorm words to do with multiplication and division. List them on the OHT.

Who can make up a multiplication problem using the word...? (Choose one of the words previously suggested by the students.)
Repeat this for other multiplication vocabulary.

Who can make up a division problem using the word..? (Choose one of the words previously suggested by the students.)
Repeat this for other division vocabulary.

A bar of...
Discuss the two problems on the OHT. Get the students to decide whether the answer is going to be bigger or smaller than the numbers in the question.

Will the answer be more or less than 12p?
Will there be more than 150 chairs in a row?

Ella runs...
Identify the key words that tell us whether to multiply or divide. (Multiplication problems usually use unitary information followed by the need to find a multiple. The word 'each' is often used.)
Explain that the way words are used can change them from a multiplication to a division problem. (Copymaster 31 gives questions to practise this point.)

Each ticket...
Look at the next two problems on the OHT. Discuss ways of solving them.

What are the key parts that tell us whether we will multiply or divide?

Ask the students to underline key words.

How do we know we need to multiply/divide?
What will the answer be?
Do we expect the answer to be more or less than this number in the question? Why?

A minibus...
Follow the same method used for the previous question.
Get the students to use the vocabulary by making up their own problems.

Who can make up a division problem using the word 'each'?
Who can make up a multiplication problem using the word 'each'?

Ask the students to suggest problems for the others to work out and check.

Solving problems: *vocabulary of multiply and divide*

Multiplication	Division

A bar of chocolate costs 12p.
How much will 9 bars cost?

There are 150 chairs in 10 rows.
How many chairs are there in each row?

Ella runs 45m. Marian runs 5 times as far.
How far does Marian run?

Pavit has collected 80 stickers.
This is 5 times more than Hilary.
How many stickers has Hilary collected?

Each ticket for a show is £18.
The family needs 6 tickets.
How much does it cost the family?

Huw buys 7 tickets for a show and they cost
him £119. How much does each ticket cost?

A minibus carries 16 people.
How many people can 8 minibuses carry?

117 people want to go on a trip.
A People Carrier can take 9 people.
How many Carriers are needed?

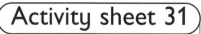

Solving problems: *vocabulary of multiply and divide*

Name _____

1a. A model car cost £2.25. How much would 5 cost? _____

1b. If 5 model cars cost £25, how much does each one cost? _____

2a. To make a cake Holly needs 250g of sugar. How much sugar does she

   need to make 6 cakes? _____

2b. Andy uses 570g of sugar to make 6 cakes. How much sugar is in each

   cake? _____

3a. Eddy saves an equal amount each week. After 8 weeks he has £9.60.

   How much did he save each week? _____

3b. Ali saves £1.35 a week for 8 weeks. How much has he saved? _____

4a. The perimeter of a regular 7 sided shape is 133cm. What is the length

   of each side? _____

4b. What is the perimeter of a regular 7 sided shape if each side is 17cm

   long? _____

5a. A full bottle holds 500ml. If 4 glasses can be filled from the bottle,

   how much does each glass hold? _____

5b. Anne has 4 glasses and each glass holds 175ml. If she fills all of them,

   how much drink has she used? _____

6a. Asmat runs a lap of the playground in 74 seconds. If she continues to

   run at that speed, how long will it take her to run 9 laps? _____

6b. Gwen runs 9 laps of the playground in 639 seconds. How long did she

   take to run each lap? _____

Solving problems: *vocabulary of multiply and divide*

Name _____

1. A coach can carry 53 people. How many people can travel on 9 coaches? _____

2. In a primary school there are 29 students in each class. There are 6 classes. How many students are at the school? _____

3. The local hockey club had 245 people in the crowd on Saturday. The town football team had 3 times as many spectators. How many people watched the football? _____

4. A CD rack can hold 24 CDs on each of its 6 shelves. How many CDs can it hold? _____

5. Ralph read his 328 page book in 8 days. He read the same number of pages each day. How many pages did he read a day? _____

6. Robby played on his computer for 55 minutes a day for 15 days. How much time did he spend on the computer? _____

7. At a theme park, Terror Tower can carry 35 people each time. If it operates 16 times, how many people can ride on it? _____

8. Stephen uses 920ml of paint for his 8 models. How much paint did he use on each one? _____

9. Each teddy has a 35cm ribbon round its neck. How much ribbon is needed for 26 teddies? _____

10. At the village dog show, 291m of rope is used to mark out the 3 rings. How much rope is used for each ring? _____

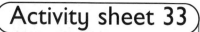

Solving problems: *vocabulary of multiply and divide*

Name _____

1. A packet of sweets costs 9p. How many can Kim buy with £1.26?

   _____

2. A train can carry a total of 312 passengers in 6 carriages. How many people can travel in each carriage? _____

3. Sally helps her dad to build a rectangular patio. It has 16 slabs along one side and 12 slabs along the other. How many slabs do they lay altogether? _____

4. To fence a field Bill needs 3 times as many rails as posts. If he needs 87 rails, how many posts does he need? _____

5. A kiddy meal at the Drive-Thru costs £2.45. How much will 6 kiddy meals cost? _____

6. Mary saves three quarters of her birthday money. If she receives £106, how much does she save? _____

7. The local factory produces 49 Ultimate Kites per week. How many does it produce in a year? _____

8. Roy earns £5.75 a week for 7 weeks washing cars. How much has he earned altogether? _____

9. A rope 87m long is cut into 3 equal pieces. How long is each piece?

   _____

10. At the school sports day 138 students take part in the races. There are 6 students in each race. How many races are there? _____

Solving problems: *vocabulary of multiply and divide*

Name

1. Ellen earns £16 980 a year, but her sister only earns half as much. How much does her sister earn?

   _____

2. Each tyre, including the spare, on a car cost £46.50. What is the total cost of the 5 new tyres? _____

3. Tickets to a concert cost £24.99 each. An entertainment company buys 27 of them. How much do they pay? _____

4. On a Sunday, a traffic census counts 4695 cars past a check point. On the following day, 3 times as many cars pass the point. How many pass on Monday? _____

5. Alan saves 50p coins. He has saved 38 of them. How much money has he saved? _____

6. The Scream Machine carries 18 people on each ride. How many people can it carry on 122 rides? _____

7. The perimeter of a regular hexagon is 75cm. What is the length of each side? _____

8. A museum has an average of 470 visitors a month. How many people visit the museum in a year? _____

9. Carl needs 75g of sugar per person for his deluxe pudding. How much sugar will he need if 17 people order the deluxe pudding? _____

10. Jackie completes 14 sit-ups in 84 seconds. How long does each sit-up take? _____

Solving problems: *vocabulary of multiply and divide*

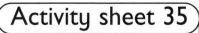

Name _____

1. Luke saves 20p coins. He has saved £13.20. How many coins has he saved? _____

2. The Loopy Line ride carries 22 people on each run. If it carried 572 people one day, how many times did it run? _____

3. Wendy needs 125g of rice for each portion of her risotto. If she used 875g, how many portions did she make? _____

4. On a Monday, 11564 cars use a multi-storey car park. On the following Sunday, a quarter of that number use the car park. How many use it on Sunday? _____

5. Isaac earns £12450 a year, but his brother earns twice as much. How much does his brother earn? _____

6. To replace the tyres, including the spare, on a car cost £178.60. What is the cost of each of the 5 new tyres? _____

7. The length of each side of a regular pentagon is 23·5cm. What is the perimeter? _____

8. A library has 7072 visitors in a year. How many people on average visit the library each week? _____

9. An entertainment company buys 17 tickets to a concert. They cost £263.50. How much is each ticket? _____

10. Ashley needs a piece of wood for the lid of a box he is making. It is 5·5cm wide and 8·2 cm long. What is the area of the lid? _____

27 + 39 = ___

Ask a student to solve the sum. Get the students to write a word problem using the sum.

Can anyone make it into an area problem? What about a money problem?

36 + 48 = ___

Ask the students to write down two or three word problems for this addition sum. Read some aloud. Get the students to identify key words for addition.

---

96 − 78 = ___

Ask a student to solve the problem. Get the students to write word problems.

Who can make it a 'difference' problem? What about a 'decrease' problem? Can anyone use length to make a problem?

87 − 59 = ___

Ask the students to write down a few possible problems for this subtraction calculation. Read some aloud and ask them to identify how they know these were subtraction problems.

---

15 × 4 = ___

Ask a student to solve the calculation. Get the class to wrap it up in a word problem. *How might a builder come across this problem? What about a dressmaker? Shopkeeper?*

5 × 16 = ___

Ask the students to write problems to do with a sports centre, a leisure park, etc. (e.g. *'16 people can swim each hour. How many people can swim in 5 hours?'*)

---

90 ÷ 6 = ___

Ask a student to solve the calculation. Then ask the students to wrap it up in a word problem.

How might a hotel manager come across this problem? What about an athlete or a farmer?

72 ÷ 4 = ___

Challenge the students to write problems to do with a farm, an airport, etc.

Use the two word problems on the OHT to identify key vocabulary needed to solve the problem.

Solving problems: *single step*

27 + 39 = ___

36 + 48 = ___

96 − 78 = ___

87 − 59 = ___

15 × 4 = ___

5 × 16 = ___

90 ÷ 6 = ___

72 ÷ 4 = ___

Sam buys 2 packs of batteries that cost 98p a pack.
How much does he pay?

Sam buys 2 packs of batteries and these cost him
98p. How much was each pack?

Solving problems: *single step*

Name _____

1. Andrew bought 3 packs of 8 postcards. How many cards did he get?

   _____

2. Pluto bars are sold in packs of 6. If Charlotte has 24 bars, how many

   packs did she buy? _____

3. Alan buys a pair of shoes for £35.99 and a sweatshirt for £12.50.

   How much has he spent altogether? _____

4. A glass holding 275ml is filled from a bottle holding 1250ml of

   lemonade. How much lemonade is left in the bottle? _____

5. A lap of the garden is 68m. Jo runs 9 laps. How far has she run?

   _____

6. Year 7 go camping. There are 133 children. Each tent sleeps 7.

   How many tents do they need? _____

7. A River Thames cruiser can carry 224 passengers. There are 137 on

   board. How many more can it carry? _____

8. Kevin jogs 14km a day. How far does he jog in a week? _____

9. Beth saves £96 at the rate of £6 a week. How long did it take her?

   _____

10. In three cricket matches Billy scores 47, 56 and 39 runs. How many has

    he scored altogether? _____

Solving problems: *single step*

Name _____

1. A lap of the swimming pool is 75m. John swims 6 laps. How far has he

    swum? _____

2. Floppy disks are sold in packs of 8. If Charlie has 32 disks, how many

    packs did he buy? _____

3. Kerry bought 7 packs of 4 stamps. How many stamps did she get?

    _____

4. What is the perimeter of this triangle? _____

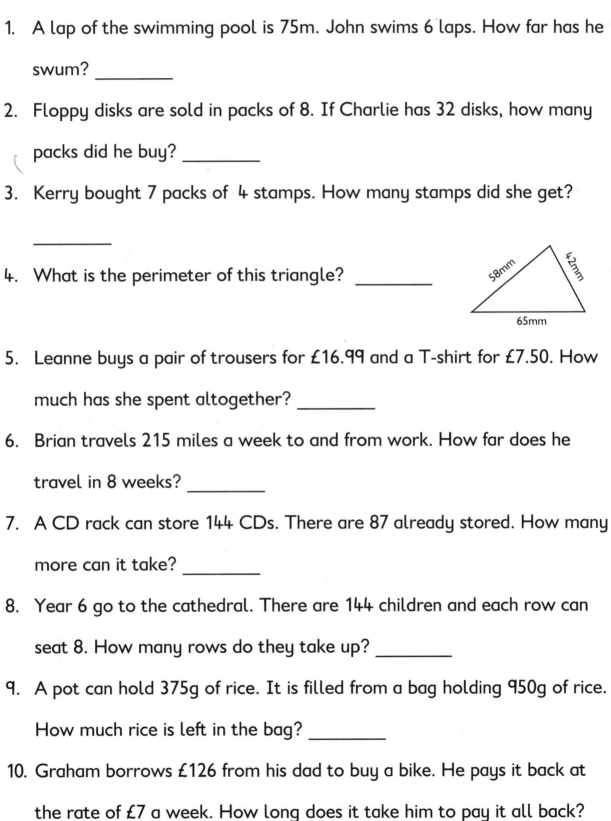

5. Leanne buys a pair of trousers for £16.99 and a T-shirt for £7.50. How

    much has she spent altogether? _____

6. Brian travels 215 miles a week to and from work. How far does he

    travel in 8 weeks? _____

7. A CD rack can store 144 CDs. There are 87 already stored. How many

    more can it take? _____

8. Year 6 go to the cathedral. There are 144 children and each row can

    seat 8. How many rows do they take up? _____

9. A pot can hold 375g of rice. It is filled from a bag holding 950g of rice.

    How much rice is left in the bag? _____

10. Graham borrows £126 from his dad to buy a bike. He pays it back at

    the rate of £7 a week. How long does it take him to pay it all back?

    _____

Solving problems: *single step*

Name _____

1. A teacher bought 13 packs of 6 pencils. How many pencils did he get?

    _____

2. Chairs in the school hall are stacked 6 high. If there are 216 chairs all

    neatly stacked, how many stacks are there? _____

3. Amy buys a pair of shorts for £15.49 and a skirt for £13.99. How much

    has she spent altogether? _____

4. An oil tank which can hold 950l of oil is filled from a tanker holding

    4040l. How much is left in the tanker? _____

5. A lap of the school field is 345m. Lesley cycles 4 laps. How far has she

    cycled? _____

6. A gardener has 135 new plants. He plants them in groups with 5 plants

    in each row. How many groups will there be? _____

7. An advertising agent has 365 envelopes to seal. He does 196 before

    coffee. How many has he left to seal? _____

8. At an outdoor pursuits centre, 58 people go climbing each month. How

    many climb in a year? _____

9. A baker packs cakes in boxes of 6. How many boxes can he fill with

    138 cakes? _____

10. In a darts match Erica scores 146, 98, and 135. What has she

    scored altogether? _____

Solving problems: *single step*

Name _____

1. A theatre sold 60 tickets at £3.75 each. How much

   money did they take? _____

2. A bag of oven chips weighs 1·81kg. How much will 8

   bags weigh? _____ .

3. A shopkeeper sells a bar of chocolate for 95p, a pack of sweets for

   £1.35 and a drink for 70p. How much does he charge altogether?

   _____

4. A rocket sets off to travel 384 401km, from Earth to the moon. After

   travelling 9877km how far has it left to travel? _____

5. A lap of the school field is 125.5m. When training for the 1800m race Ali

   runs 13 laps. How far has he run? _____

6. A building site needs 75 000 bricks. A lorry can carry 12 500 bricks at a

   time. How many deliveries will be needed? _____

7. A swimming pool holds 455 000l of water. How much water is in the

   pool when it is half full? _____

8. An energetic snail crawls 9·75m a day. How far does he crawl

   in a week? _____

9. A ream of 500 sheets of paper weighs 750g. What does each

   sheet weigh? _____

10. A crate of 24 bottles costs £8.40. How much does each bottle cost?

    _____

Solving problems: *single step*

Name _____

1. A company manager's salary is increased by £2650 to £34 995. What was her salary before the increase?

   _____

2. Julian saves 50 pence pieces. He has saved 27 of them. How much money has he saved? _____

3. Sharon's pigs eat a sack of food every week. If a sack of food costs £5.25, how much does it cost to feed her pigs for a year? _____

4. A bag of sweets weighs 454g. How much will 12 bags weigh? _____

5. In a four person relay the times of the laps were as follows: Linda 41·2 seconds, Alice 39·9 seconds, Gerry 44·1 seconds, Kate 38·6 seconds. How long did the race take? _____

6. A cotton reel has a circumference of 7·5cm. How many times will a piece of cotton measuring 195cm go around the reel? _____

7. The reading on a car's milometer is 76 504 miles. Two months ago, the reading was 74 099 miles. How far has the car travelled in two months? _____

8. A crate of 16 cans costs £7.20. How much does each can cost?

   _____

9. A show jumper completes a jump off in 43·21 seconds. The next competitor was 3·9 seconds slower. How long did the second rider take to complete the jump? _____

10. A gallery sold 45 tickets at £2.25 each. How much money did they take? _____

Some word problems give more information than is necessary. Students need to be able to find the relevant information. A highlighter pen is a valuable tool for this work.

On Monday morning...

Read the problem together. Get the students to underline relevant information and to cross out irrelevant information.

Do we need to know the date that this happened?
What are we actually asked to find out?
Who can cross out some more irrelevant information?
What is the answer?

I had £10...

This is the previous question with all the unnecessary information removed. Challenge the students to write their own story problems.

On Monday 28th...

Repeat the above method with this problem. Use highlighting and crossing out to sort the information.

Can someone cross out a piece of information we do not need?
Do we need to know the date he placed the order?
Is the question about costs or money?
What is the question actually about?
What is the answer?

What is the date...

Reveal the simplified question.

Bus information...

Hide the question and read through the information together. Ask the students what the question could be about. This is a valuable way of getting the students to really read the information first.
Disclose the question.

Which part of the bus information is totally irrelevant?
What is the answer?

Challenge the students to write their own story problems. This time, get them to hide the final question and ask a friend to predict what the question might be using the information given in the problem.

Solving problems:
relevant information

On Monday morning, 24th March, my brother Jack took the number 17 bus to town. He arrived there at 09:30. The journey had taken him 20 minutes. He had £10 in his pocket and wanted to buy a book. He entered the book shop at 09:50 and took 25 minutes choosing a book which cost him £5.99. How much change did he receive?

I had £10 and bought a book for £5.99. How much change did I receive?

On Monday, 28th May, a builder placed an order for some materials. He needed 15 lengths of 2·4m wood, 4 cubic metres of cement at £49 per cubic metre and a 50m sheet of damp course. The delivery took 5 days to arrive. On what date did it arrive?

What is the date 5 days after the 28th May?

Bus information			
Appleton	09:15	09:25	09:50
Bidford	09:28	09:40	10:04
Cardon	09:40	09:52	10:16

A single fare from Appleton to Bidford is 53p.
A single fare from Appleton to Cardon is 87p.

How much does it cost 3 people to go from Appleton to Cardon?

Solving problems:
relevant information

Name _____

Underline the important information in the story problems. Cross out the parts you do not need, and answer the questions.

1. Jo looked out of her bedroom window at 07:00 on Tuesday, 27th of August. It was 120m to the end of the garden, and the end of the drive lay 75m beyond that. The letter box at the end of the drive would hold her birthday cards in exactly one week's time. If she ran fast, she could reach it in 30 seconds. What was the date of her birthday? _____

2. Bobby's class of 32 students went camping on June 16th for 5 days. They travelled 73 miles and it took them 2 hours 15 minutes to get to the campsite. It cost £1.20 per person per night and it rained every day. Each tent held 8 students. How many tents did they need?

   _____

Now answer these.

3. Rulers cost 27p and sharpeners cost 18p. Sharon buys 6 rulers. How much do they cost? _____

4. Last week at North School, Yellow house had 143 points, Blue house had 76 points and Red house had 87 points. How many more points did Yellow have than Red? _____

5. Morag had £29.50 for her birthday, and she already had £37.84. Her brother had £16.90. How much has Morag altogether? _____

6. When baking biscuits, Laura needed 455g of flour, 290g of sugar and 250g of butter. How much more flour than sugar did she need?

   _____

7. The hall was set out with 144 chairs and 15 tables. There were 9 chairs in each row. How many rows were there? _____

Solving problems:
relevant information

Name

Underline the important information in the story problems. Cross out the parts you do not need, and answer the questions.

1. Wayne and Harry were collecting Dream Trainer cards. They cost 75p for a pack of 5 Ultimate cards or 80p for a pack of 15 Topic cards. Wayne had a total of 65 cards, but Harry only had 35 cards. How much was each Ultimate card? _____

2. Emily built an obstacle course to do on her bike. It was 250m long with 12 obstacles on the route. She cycled the course 9 times in one day and her best time was 42 seconds. On 13th February, she invited her friend Sarah to try out the course, and she took 1 minute 4 seconds to complete it.
   How much longer did Sarah take than Emily? _____

Now answer these.

3. Michael got home from school at 4.15 p.m. He did his homework for 50 minutes and then played football for 45 minutes. At what time did he finish his homework? _____

4. Eric built a wall 6 bricks high. Each layer was 24 bricks long. Each brick was 10cm high. How many bricks were in the wall? _____

5. Notepads cost 55p, pencils cost 15p. How many pencils can Fred buy for 90p? _____

6. A zoo keeps 17 snakes in 9 tanks. If each snake eats 5 mice how many mice have been eaten? _____

7. Doctor Jones started work at 9 a.m. and saw 105 patients one day and 76 patients the next day. How many patients did he see altogether?

   _____

Solving problems:
relevant information

Name

Underline the important information in the story problems. Cross out the parts you do not need, and answer the questions.

1. Amir, aged 12, bought a computer game for £29.50. His bus journey back from town took 18 minutes and he arrived home at 14:15 with only £3.01 left in his pocket. He looked in his computer magazine and saw the same game for £25.99, including postage. How much would he have saved if he had bought the game from the magazine? _____

2. The farm was 37km from the nearest town and it usually took Peter about 35 minutes to get there if he had a good run. He left at 10:35, but stopped for petrol and put in 25l and bought a 5l can of oil. This put an extra 5 minutes on the journey. How far was the journey to town and back? _____

Now answer these.

3. Fay poured 7 drinks of lemonade, each drink was 250ml. A bottle of lemonade cost 87p. How much lemonade did she need? _____

4. When fencing a field the farmer needed 3 rolls of wire and 40 posts. The total cost of wire was £102. The posts were £2.70 each. How much was each roll of wire? _____

5. Jo started her homework at 16:35. After 35 minutes she stopped for a drink. She then continued her homework for a further 45 minutes. What time did she stop for a drink? _____

6. A school play had an audience of 234 on the first night, 198 on the second and 256 on the final night. How many more people attended the final night than the second night? _____

7. A camping shop sold 17 tents, 29 backpacks and 24 sleeping bags. The following month 4 times as many backpacks were sold. How many was that? _____

Solving problems:
relevant information

Name _____

1. Susan bought a computer for £1029.50. The printer cost an extra £249.99 and the scanner was £199.00. She looked in her computer magazine and saw the same computer for £1125.99, including delivery. How much cheaper was the computer in the shop than in the magazine? _____

2. Adam lived 47km from his place of work. The journey took him 45 minutes on average. How far did he travel to and from work during a 5-day week? _____

3. Carol was regularly given 50p coins by her grandparents. When she counted them up she had 35 coins. She also collected 20p coins and she had 27 of them. How much money had her grandparents given her? _____

4. Harry went to buy a secondhand car. The first one he looked at was £3599 and had 76 503 miles on the clock. The second one had 83 942 on the clock and was £3075. How many more miles had the second car travelled than the first? _____

5. The entry fee at the local horse show was £3.50 per horse. Linda completed a clear round in 35·8 seconds and won second prize. Altogether 73 horses entered the show. How much money did they take? _____

6. Cardiff to Norwich is 4 times further than Cardiff to Gloucester. How far is it from Cardiff to Norwich? _____

7. A ticket to the school play is £2.45. The play started at 7.30 p.m. and lasted 1 hour 45 minutes. On Tuesday night 70 people attended the play . How much money was taken? _____

Gloucester

65 miles

36 miles

Cardiff

47 miles

Bristol

Solving problems:
relevant information

Name

1. Sanjit was collecting Fire Master cards. He had 18 Grand Masters and 36 Servers. Grand Masters were 75p for a pack of 3 cards. The Servers had cost him £3.24. How much was each Server? _____

2. In a local shop CDs cost £13 each and tapes cost £8.45. The shop was open from 08:30 to 18:30. If Megan bought 5 tapes how much did she pay? _____

3. Barry travelled 27 miles each way to work, 6 days a week. The journey took 40 minutes. On Thursday he arrived home at 7.15 p.m. What time did he leave work? _____

4. Ben collected 20p coins and he had 27 of them. He also had a jar for 50p coins. When he counted up the 50p coins he had £22.50. How many coins was that? _____

5. The price of Jenny's new car was £9059. Her old car had 98 000 miles on the clock and the garage gave her £1590 off the new car price for it. How much did she pay? _____

6. A party of 27 adults went to Malton Towers for the day. How much did it cost them to get in? _____

	Malton Towers	Shorpe Park
Adult	£18.50	£17.00
Child under 9	£9.25	£9.50
Opening times	09:30 – 20:00	09:00 – 20:30

7. A salesman travels from Carlisle to Dover and then from Dover to Cardiff. How far has he travelled?

   _____

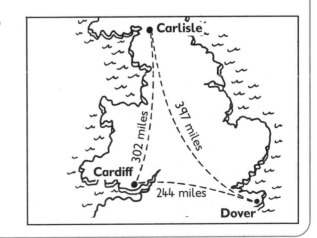

1cm...

Revise work done on the relationships between the units.

Do some quick-fire conversion questions with the students.

Convert 5m... 9m... 1·3m... 5·7m... 4·25m... to centimetres.
Convert 3kg... 7kg... 2·5kg... 6·8kg... 3·25kg...to grams.
Convert 3km... 8km... 1·2km... 4·9km... 3·75km... to metres.

Remind them to use their visual understanding to check the sense of their answers.

What is half...

Practise converting to the smaller unit. Write the decimal version alongside.

1cm   5mm   0·5cm

For 1·000kg write 500g and 0·500kg to help the students see the link. Eventually they will use 0·5kg.

What about...

The students should learn these equivalents.

What is a quarter of a metre as a decimal of a metre?
What is a quarter of a metre in centimetres?

You may want to use a table like this for students to complete themselves as practice.

Add 1·5m...

Converting units is an important skill that is very often overlooked.

What do we need to do before we can work out the addition sum?
Which unit will we convert to? Why?

Add £2.24...

What do we need to do before we can work out the addition sum?
Which unit will we convert to? Why?

What is the difference...

What do you expect the answer to be?
Which one will we convert?
What will it be now?

What is...

What operation will we need to use to solve this problem?
Which quantity will we convert?

Solving problems:
changing units

1cm = ___ mm   1m = ___ cm

1m = ___ mm   1km = ___ m

1kg = ___ g   1l = ___ ml

What is half of each of these?

1 cm ___ mm   1 m ___ mm

1 litre ___ ml   1kg ___ g

What about these?

	quarter	3 quarters	tenth
1m			
1km			
1litre			
1kg			

Add 1·5m and 35cm.

Add £2.24 and 78p.

What is the difference between 1·3km and 895m?

What is 450ml less than 1·2 litres?

Solving problems:
changing units

Name _____

1. Fill in the missing numbers.

   2·4m = _____ cm   3·2kg = _____ g   42mm = _____ cm

   £2.76 = _____ p   5600ml = _____ litres   3500g = _____ kg

2. How many millilitres are there in a quarter of a litre? _____

3. How many grams are there in three quarters of a kilogram? _____

4. How many centimetres are there in a tenth of a metre? _____

5. Padam bought the following items:

   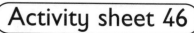

   £1.25   £2.99   89p

   How much did she spend altogether? _____

6. Henry weighed out some ingredients for a large cake. He had 1·2kg of
   flour, 600g of sugar and 350g of sultanas. How much more did the flour
   weigh than the sultanas? _____

7. A full bucket holds 4 and a half litres. My jug holds 500ml. How many
   times can I fill my jug from the bucket? _____

8. Daniel bought a 2kg bag of potatoes. He used 750g of them for dinner.
   What weight of potatoes was left? _____

9. On the journey home from his holiday, Leroy travelled by plane for
   2 and a half hours and by coach for 50 minutes. How long was he
   travelling? _____

10. What is the perimeter of

    the rectangle? _____

    52mm

    2·4cm

Solving problems:
changing units

Name _____

1. Fill in the missing numbers.

    50mm = _____ cm   7·5 l = _____ ml   3·7m = _____ cm

    350p = £_____   8500m = _____ km   5·5cm = _____ mm

2. How many grams are there in a tenth of a kilogram? _____

3. How many metres are there in three quarters of a kilometre? _____

4. How many millimetres are there in a quarter of a metre? _____

5. A cake tin holds 1·3kg of mixture. Jan puts 820g of mixture into

    the tin. How much more can she put in? _____

6. Yasmin was making a tropical punch drink. She poured in 1·5l of

    lemonade, 750ml of orange juice and 125ml of lemon squash. How

    much tropical punch did she have? _____

7. Melanie bought the following items:

    £2.99   85p   £3.49

    How much did she spend altogether? _____

8. How many 250ml cups can be filled from a 2·5l jug? _____

9. What is the perimeter of the triangle? _____

    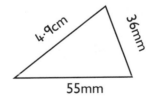

    4·9cm   36mm   55mm

10. On his journey to work Barry travelled by train for 1 and a quarter

    hours and by foot for 25 minutes. How long did it take him to get to

    work? _____

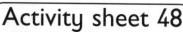

Solving problems:
changing units

Name _____

1. Fill in the missing numbers.

    £8.55 = ____ p   7·4kg = ____ g   4100g = ____ kg

    3·2m = ____ cm   4300ml = ____ litres   135mm = ____ cm

2. How many millimetres are there in a tenth of a metre? _____

3. How many centimetres are there in three quarters of a metre?

    _____

4. How many millilitres are there in half a litre? _____

5. Nina bought the following items:

    How much did she spend

    altogether? _____

    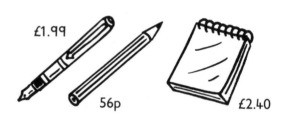

    £1.99   56p   £2.40

6. Ella feeds her cats 250g of cat food at each meal. How many meals can

    she make from a 5kg bag of cat food? _____

7. A full bucket holds 5l. My jug holds 200ml. How many times can I fill

    my jug from the bucket? _____

8. Diane bought a 3kg bag of carrots. She used 625g of them for lunch.

    What weight of carrots was left? _____

9. When Alan got home from school he played football for 1 and

    three-quarter hours and then played basketball for 35 minutes. How

    long did he play altogether ? _____

10. What is the area of the rectangle? _____   2·3cm

    9mm

Solving problems:
changing units

Name _____

1. Julia is 94cm tall. Eddie is 1·72m tall. What is the

   difference in their heights? _____

2. Baby Ravi is 850g heavier than Jack. Jack weighs

   5·42kg. How heavy is Ravi? _____

3. Bobby earns 85p for emptying the dishwasher. How many times will

   he need to empty the dishwasher to earn £10.20? _____

4. How many pieces of string 45cm long can be cut from a piece of string

   6·75m long? _____

5. Wendy has a 1·4kg bag of flour. She needs 175g of flour for each batch

   of pancakes. How many batches of pancakes can she make? _____

6. Sam takes 75 seconds to run each lap of the field. If he runs 4 laps for

   how many minutes has he been running? _____

7. The perimeter of a square is 2·1m. How many centimetres long is

   each side? _____

8. Fred saved 35p a week for one year. How many pounds did he save?

   _____

9. If 1·28 litres of milk are used to make 4 milkshakes, how many

   millilitres of milk are used in each one? _____

10. It takes Rachel 4 minutes and 10 seconds to finish her speed maths test.

    She completes 50 questions. How many seconds did she take on each

    question? _____

Solving problems:
changing units

Name _____

1. The perimeter of a rectangle is 3·2m. The shortest sides are 72cm each. What is the length of each of the longest sides? _____

2. The fence along one side of a farmer's land is 1·35km long. The fence along another side is 82m shorter. How long is the shorter fence? _____

3. Ricky earns 65p for emptying the bins. How many times will he need to empty the bins to earn £5.20? _____

4. A piece of ribbon 55cm long is tied round each teddy's neck. If there are 15 teddies, how many metres of ribbon are needed? _____

5. Lucy has a 3kg bag of pasta. She needs 125g of pasta for each portion. How many portions can she cook? _____

6. Kelly buys 3 packets of sweets for 56p each. How much change does she get from £5? _____

7. The perimeter of a square is 1·42m. How many centimetres long is each side? _____

8. Nicola saved 37p a week for one year. How many pounds did she save?

   _____

9. At a party 75ml of cordial is used to make each child's drink. How many litres of cordial are used if 36 drinks are made? _____

10. It takes Rebecca 4 minutes to type 80 words. How many seconds did she take to type each word? _____

The key to solving multi-step problems is what to find out first. Students need to practise breaking down/splitting up the problem into the obvious question and the hidden step or steps to get to the answer.

I buy a pen...
Uncover the question only. Ask the students what they need to find out first. Then work through the OHT. Get the students to suggest their own problems in a similar format. Write some on the board and get the children to explain how to solve them.

I need £9.99...
What do we need to know first?
How can we find out how much has been saved?
What do we do next?

Get the students to write their own problems in a similar format for each other to solve.

I think of a number...
The students need a clear grasp of inverse operations to handle these types of problems efficiently.

I think of a number, multiply it by 4, then add 6. The answer is 30. What is my number? (6)
Who can draw the diagram for the question?

___ × 4 + 6 = 30

Who can draw the inverse route to work out the answer?

30 − 6 ÷ 4 = ___

I think of a number, multiply it by 6, then subtract 7. The answer is 35.
What is my number? (7)
I think of a number, add 12, then divide it by 4. The answer is 6. What is my number? (12)

Many problems where the starting number is missing are best solved in this way. Start at the beginning, list what happens through the problem, then work in reverse to find the missing number.

Recipe for...
How could we find out what is needed for 1 cake?
What about 2 cakes? Which is more useful if we need to make 6 cakes?
What if I rewrote the recipe and it had 5 eggs, how much sugar would there be then?

Practise working with simple recipes, e.g. for concrete.

Solving problems: *multi-step*

I buy a pen for 35p and a pad for 47p.
How much change do I get from £1?

How much do I spend? $35 + 47 =$
How much change?

I need £9.99 to buy a tape. I save £3.50
one week and £4.65 the next. How much
more do I need?

How much have I saved so far?
$£3.50 + £4.65 =$

How much more?

I think of a number, add 15 and divide by
3. The answer is 7. What was my number?

☐ —| + 15 〉— ÷ 3 〉— 7

7 —| × 3 〉— − 15 〉— ☐

Recipe for 4 mini cakes
   120g flour
   120g margarine
   100g sugar
   2 eggs

How much of each is needed for 6 cakes?

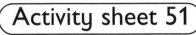

Solving problems: *multi-step*

Name

1. Robbie buys a CD for £12 and a book for £6.35. How much has he got left from £20? _____

2. I had £5 pocket money. I spent half on a magazine, and one fifth on sweets. How much did I have left? _____

3. From a plank 2·4m long, Dave cuts a piece 1·3m and another piece 0·5m long. How much of the plank is left? _____

4. The sun sets at 19:50. Aled goes to bed 45 minutes later and then takes 20 minutes to get to sleep. At what time does he fall asleep? _____

5. Billie buys 4 packets of sweets for £1.60. How much would it cost for 6 packets of the same sweets? _____

6. In my vegetable patch I have room for 6 rows of beans with 12 beans in each row along one side, and enough room for twice as many along the other side. How many bean plants is that altogether? _____

7. I think of a number, subtract 18 and divide by 9. The answer is 7. What was my number? _____

8. Adrian starts to read a book on Tuesday. On Wednesday, he reads 11 pages more than on Tuesday. He reaches page 35. How many pages did he read on Tuesday? _____

9. I think of a number, multiply by 4 and add 12. The answer is 48. What was my number? _____

10. Alison bought 36 eggs. She used a sixth of them in some cakes and scrambled one quarter of them for tea. How many eggs did she have left? _____

Solving problems: *multi-step*

Name _____

1. The bus sets off at 10:50. It stops 35 minutes later and waits for 25 minutes before setting off again. At what time does it set off again? _____

2. I owed my brother £9. I gave him half one week, and one sixth the next. How much did I still owe him? _____

3. From a rope 3·5m long, Alex cuts a piece 1·4m and another piece 0·9m long. How much of the rope is left? _____

4. Eleanor buys a hutch for £15 and a rabbit for £18.50. How much has she left from £35? _____

5. A recipe for 4 people requires 150g flour. How much flour will be needed for 6 people? _____

6. Edward bought 40 daffodil bulbs. He planted one fifth of them in some pots and one quarter of them in the front flower bed. How many bulbs did he have left? _____

7. I think of a number, subtract 23 and divide by 7. The answer is 5. What was my number? _____

8. In a two man relay the second runner takes 10 seconds longer than the first. The whole race takes 72 seconds. How long does the first runner take? _____

9. I think of a number, multiply by 6 and add 17. The answer is 59. What was my number? _____

10. Mary starts to read a book on Thursday. On Friday, she reads 15 more pages than on Thursday. She reaches page 43. How many pages did she read on Thursday? _____

Solving problems: *multi-step*

Name _____

1. Eric buys 2 CDs for £8.99 each. How much change does he get from £20? _____

2. I had 750g of sugar. I used half in a cake, and 125g in sweets. How much did I have left? _____

3. A family set out on a 145km journey. They stop for a snack after 83km and then stop again after another 25km. What distance have they left to travel? _____

4. Fran starts watching television at 17:30. She watches a soap opera for 35 minutes and then the news for 25 minutes. What time does she finish watching television? _____

5. When Olly feeds 6 puppies he uses 540g of meat. How much meat will he need for 9 puppies? _____

6. In a two man relay the second runner takes 16 seconds longer than the first. The whole race takes 84 seconds. How long does the second runner take? _____

7. I think of a number, subtract 26 and divide by 6. The answer is 10. What was my number? _____

8. Philip practises the piano on Tuesday. On Wednesday he practises for 6 minutes longer than on Tuesday. He practises for a total of 48 minutes. For how long did he practise on Tuesday? _____

9. Hannah bought 24 shrubs for the garden. She planted one third of them in a raised flowerbed and one sixth of them under the front window. How many did she have left to put in the back garden? _____

10. I think of a number, multiply by 9 and subtract 36. The answer is 45. What was my number? _____

Solving problems: *multi-step*

Name _____

1. Sam buys 4 CDs for £12.99 each and 5 tapes for £8.95 each. How much change does he get from £100?

   _____

2. I had 2700g of flour. I used one quarter in a cake, and 350g in biscuits. How much did I have left?

   _____

3. A charity group set out on a 95 mile sponsored walk. Each day they walk 2 miles more than the day before. On the first day they walk 15 miles. How many days does it take them? _____

4. Find three consecutive numbers that add up to 225. _____

5. Emma spends 27 minutes grooming her pony. She then spends twice as long riding him and 15 minutes cooling him off. How long has she spent with her pony? _____

6. Joanna is 112cm tall. Sally is 156cm tall. John's height is halfway between them. Calculate John's height. _____

7. I think of a number, subtract 132 and divide by 16. The answer is 15. What was my number? _____

8. In a library there are 28 shelves of science books. Of the 28 shelves, 17 hold 54 books. The rest of the shelves hold 62 books each. How many science books are there altogether? _____

9. Jim bought 3 pigs. The first pig was half as heavy as the second pig. The third pig was 3·5kg heavier than the second pig. If the third pig weighed 20·5kg, how heavy was the first pig? _____

10. I think of a number, multiply by 19 and add 243. The answer is 737. What was my number? _____

Solving problems: *multi-step*

Name _____

1. Gerry's car's milometer reads 25 899 miles. Gerry uses the car for a year, travelling an average of 550 miles a month. What is the reading on the milometer at the end of the year? _____

2. Find three consecutive numbers that add up to 261.

    _____

3. Fred needs £95.50 to buy a CD player. He saves £4.80 a week for 12 weeks. How much more does he need? _____

4. Aaron has a rope 5m long. He cuts 4 pieces each 1.1m long. How much rope is left? _____

5. Roger pours 7·5 litres of water into the horses' empty water trough. Later he pours in another 5·6 litres. At the end of the day there are 4·9 litres of water left in the trough. How much did the horses drink?

    _____

6. Jill bought 3 young trees. The first tree was three times as tall as the second tree. The third tree was 14cm taller than the first tree. If the third tree was 152cm tall how tall was the second tree? _____

7. I think of a number, add 97 and divide by 17. The answer is 19. What was my number? _____

8. In a library there are 34 shelves of history books. Of the 34 shelves, 19 hold 42 books. The rest of the shelves hold 39 books each. How many history books are there altogether? _____

9. April is 95cm tall. Camilla is 143cm tall. Habib's height is halfway between them. Calculate Habib's height. _____

10. I think of a number, divide by 16 and add 198. The answer is 244. What was my number? _____

146 ÷ 6...

Recap work on division with remainders. If division is still difficult for your children then adding the complication of rounding up or down will cause even more confusion.

Golf balls...

Drawing rough sketches of the problem can help students to decide whether to round up or down. In the first question the key word is 'filled'. In the second question the left over balls must be packed so another box is needed.

What was the answer to the division calculation?
So the answer is going to be 7 or 8. What about the 2 balls left over?

How many...

Work out the answer to the division calculation first.

What are the two possibilities for the answer?
How do we know which one is the answer?

You can not buy part of a shirt so only the whole numbers count.

An outing...

What are the two possibilities for the answer?
How do we know which one is the answer?

If there are only 27 cars then some people are left behind.

How many...

Practise dividing numbers. Explain the difference between rounding numbers (5 and above always round up) compared to rounding an answer in context.

130 ÷ 24 = 5·41666 *so what two numbers could the answer be?*
Each piece of string must be 24cm long so have we got enough for 6?

Each table...

Will the answer be 5 or 6?
How do we know?

In this case the extra people would have nowhere to sit if there were only 5 tables.

Solving problems: *division*

$$\frac{146}{6} \qquad 6\overline{)146}$$

$$\frac{133}{4} \qquad 4\overline{)133}$$

$$\frac{165}{9} \qquad 9\overline{)165}$$

Golf balls are sold in packs of 9. If you have 65 golf balls how many packs can be filled?

Colin needs to pack 65 golf balls. He can put 9 in each box. How many boxes does he need?

$$\frac{109}{4} \qquad 4\overline{)109}$$

How many shirts at £4 each can a shop buy for £109?

An outing is planned for 109 people. They travel in cars with 4 people in a car. How many cars are needed?

How many pieces of string 24cm long can be cut from a string 130 cm long?

Each table in a restaurant can seat 24 people. How many tables are needed to seat 130 people?

Solving problems: *division*

Name _____

1. If 5 people can travel in a car, how many cars are needed for

    38 people to go on a trip? _____

2. A teacher needs 68 pencils for her class. A box has 12 pencils in it. How

    many boxes must she buy? _____

3. Tracey has saved £75. Tickets to the local concert are £8 each. How

    many tickets can she buy? _____

4. Derek has 1500g of flour. If each cake needs 200g of flour, how many

    cakes can he bake? _____

5. In a sports hall, badminton courts are hired for 50 minutes per session.

    If one game of badminton takes 9 minutes how many complete games

    can be played in a session? _____

6. A window box can hold 9 plants. How many window boxes can be

    filled with 146 plants? _____

7. Mandy has collected 85 eggs. She packs them in boxes of 6. How many

    boxes can she fill? _____

8. A ribbon 125 cm long is cut into pieces 9cm long to decorate a dress.

    How many pieces 9cm long can be cut? _____

9. In a fairground a roller-coaster can carry 8 people on each run. How

    many runs will it have to make for 126 people to have a ride? _____

10. There are 170 children in the grand parade. The organiser wants to

    give them each a bar of chocolate. The bars come in packs of 6. How

    many packs does he need? _____

Solving problems: *division*

Name _____

1. A piece of wood 145cm long is cut into pieces 6cm long for a design

    project. How many pieces 6 cm long are there? _____

2. A dog breeder needs 58 chews for her dogs. A box has 10 chews in it.

    How many boxes must she buy? _____

3. If 4 people can travel in a car, how many cars are needed for

    29 people to go on a trip? _____

4. Dianne has 1800ml of juice. If each glass holds 250ml, how many

    glasses can she fill? _____

5. Tim has saved £95. Tickets to the wildlife park are £9 each. How many

    tickets can he buy? _____

6. A group of 75 scouts go camping. How many tents will be needed if

    each tent sleeps 6 scouts? _____

7. Mark has collected 115 stamps. His album takes 8 stamps per page.

    How many pages can he fill? _____

8. In a riding school, a course of cross-country jumps is hired for

    30 minutes per session. If one round of jumps takes 4 minutes how

    many complete rounds can be jumped in a session? _____

9. A pedalo can carry 5 people on each run. How many runs will it have

    to make for 88 people to have a ride? _____

10. There are 150 bulbs in a sack. The gardener wants to plant an equal

    number of bulbs in each of his 7 pots. How many bulbs can he put in

    each one? _____

Solving problems: *division*

Name _____

1. If a lift can carry 8 people, how many trips are needed for 62 people to get to a penthouse party? _____

2. A rabbit enthusiast has 38 rabbits. A hutch can house 3 rabbits. How many hutches must he have? _____

3. Jeremy has saved £86. Tickets to the zoo are £7 each. How many tickets can he buy? _____

4. A dog eats 8kg of biscuit mixer a week. For how many complete weeks will a 30kg sack last? _____

5. Basketball teams have 5 players. In a school tournament 58 children want to play. How many teams can be made? _____

6. Tesbury superstore sells oranges in bags of 7. How many bags can be filled with 135 oranges? _____

7. A traffic warden issues 9 tickets a day. How many days will it take her to issue 130 tickets? _____

8. A string 138 cm long is cut into pieces 7cm long. How many pieces 7cm long are there? _____

9. In a fairground a ghost train can carry 6 people on each run. How many runs will it have to make for 109 people to have a ride? _____

10. There are 134 children on the youth club camp. The tents can sleep 8 children. How many tents are needed? _____

Solving problems: *division*

Name _____

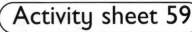

1. A party of 250 people go on a trip. A coach holds 52 people. How many coaches are needed? _____

2. In a tropical fish shop each fish tank holds a maximum of 18 fish. How many tanks are needed for 285 fish? _____

3. Malcolm has saved £230. Train tickets to London are £47 each. How many tickets can he buy? _____

4. Oliver's story is 600 words long. He can fit 140 words on each page. How many pages does he need? _____

5. Rugby teams have 15 players. In a school tournament 138 children want to play. How many teams can be made? _____

6. I have 1250g of margarine. Each batch of biscuits needs 175g of margarine. How many batches of biscuits can I make? _____

7. A computer printer takes 18 sheets of paper. How many times will the printer need loading to print a 275 page document? _____

8. A string 250 cm long is cut into pieces 28cm long. How many pieces 28cm long are there? _____

9. In a theme park a Ferris wheel can carry 26 people on each run. How many runs will it have to make for 190 people to have a ride? _____

10. If a crate can hold 24 bottles, how many crates can be filled with 275 bottles? _____

Solving problems: *division*

Name _____

1. A trip has been arranged for 307 people. A coach holds 52 people. How many coaches are needed? _____

2. In a glass shop each cabinet holds a maximum of 34 ornaments. How many cabinets are needed for 150 ornaments? _____

3. William has saved £275. Train tickets to Glasgow are £54 each. How many tickets can he buy? _____

4. A school drama club sells 150 tickets. The drama hall can seat 45 people. How many performances will they have to do? _____

5. A baker makes 270 cakes. A box holds 35 cakes. How many boxes can he fill? _____

6. I have 2850ml of milk. Each glass can hold 220ml. How many glasses can I fill? _____

7. A wedding photographer can take 24 photographs with one film. How many films will be needed for 170 photographs? _____

8. A sausage machine turns out 486 sausages into packs of 8. How many full packs of 8 sausages will this make? _____

9. A river cruiser can carry 28 passengers. How many runs will it have to make for 235 people to have a cruise? _____

10. If a box can hold 22 chocolates, how many boxes can be filled with 320 chocolates? _____

Extracting information:
money

This table shows how the prices of certain makes of trainers vary in different shops.

shops / trainers	Apple	Breaker	Challenge
Delta	£12.49	£24.00	£33.99
Eachway	£14.50	£24.50	£45.00
Franchise	£13.59	£25.99	£38.99

This table shows the takings of a school tuck shop over three months.

month / item	crisps	sweets	drinks
May	£112.00	£82.20	£130.00
June	£126.00	£112.60	£125.50
July	£143.50	£94.60	£145.50

Extracting information:
money

Name _____

This table shows how the prices of certain makes of trainers vary in different shops.

shops \ trainers	Apple	Breaker	Challenge
Delta	£12.99	£24.99	£35.99
Eachway	£14.00	£24.00	£40.00
Franchise	£13.50	£25.50	£38.50

1. Which shop sells the cheapest pair of Breakers? _____

2. How much does Delta charge for a pair of Challenge trainers?

   _____

3. Which shop sells the most expensive pair of Challenge trainers?

   _____

4. If Delta put the price of a pair of Breakers up by 98p, what would the new price be? _____

5. If Franchise cut the price of a pair of Breakers by 98p, what would the new price be? _____

6. Both Vince and Paul buy a pair of Challenge trainers at Franchise. How much do they pay altogether? _____

7. In their super sale Eachway take 25% off Breakers. How much do they cost in the sale? _____

8. Stephanie buys a pair of Apple and a pair of Challenge at Eachway. How much would she have saved if she had shopped at Franchise?

   _____

Extracting information:
money

Name _____

This table shows how the prices of certain makes of T-shirts vary in different shops.

shops \ T-shirts	Gat	Harvey	Indigo
Jolly's	£4.49	£5.99	£5.99
Kitbag	£4.00	£4.00	£5.00
Leisure	£3.50	£6.50	£3.50

1. Which shop sells the cheapest Indigo shirt? _____

2. How much does Leisure charge for a Harvey shirt? _____

3. Which shop sells the most expensive Gat shirt? _____

4. If Leisure put the price of an Indigo shirt up by 98p, what would the new price be? _____

5. If Jolly's cut the price of a Gat shirt by 98p, what would the new price be? _____

6. Phillipa, Barbara and Hannah each buy a Harvey shirt at Jolly's. How much do they pay altogether? _____

7. In their super sale Kitbag take 25% off Gat shirts. How much do they cost in the sale? _____

8. Ian buys a Gat and an Indigo shirt at Jolly's. How much would he have saved if he had shopped at Kitbag? _____

✱ Remember 25% = ¹/₄

Extracting information:
money

Name _____

This table shows how the prices of certain makes of jackets vary in different shops.

shops ╲ jackets	Macho	Nelson	Park
Riverside	£52.49	£54.49	£65.49
Salter's	£63.50	£55.50	£58.50
Telling	£54.00	£54.00	£60.00

1. Which shop sells the cheapest Park jacket? _____

2. How much does Riverside charge for a Nelson jacket? _____

3. Which shop sells the most expensive Macho jacket? _____

4. If Salter's put the price of a Macho up by 98p, what would the new price be? _____

5. If Telling cut the price of a Nelson by 98p, what would the new price be? _____

6. Riverside sells 4 Park jackets. How much money do they take altogether? _____

7. In their super sale Salter's take 10% off a Park jacket. How much does it cost in the sale? _____

8. How much cheaper would it be to buy a Macho and a Nelson jacket at Riverside rather than at Salter's? _____

Extracting information:
money

Name _____

The table shows the takings of a school tuck shop over three months.

month \ item	crisps	sweets	drinks
May	£120.60	£95.20	£150.00
June	£126.00	£110.40	£135.50
July	£147.60	£95.20	£160.00

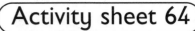

1. How much was taken in June on sweets alone?

   _____

2. How much money was taken in May altogether?

   _____

3. What was the total taken for sweet sales over the three-

   month period? _____

4. Last December the tuck shop took twice as much money for sweets as

   in May. How much was taken in December? _____

5. In April only half as much was taken for crisp sales as in July. How

   much was taken in April? _____

6. Drinks cost 50p each. How many were sold in June? _____

7. In May, 335 packets of crisps were sold. How much did each packet

   cost? _____

8. Only 10% of the takings are profit. How much profit was made on

   crisps in May? _____

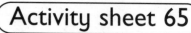

Extracting information:
money

Name

The table shows the takings of a school stationery shop over three months.

month \ item	pens	pencils	pads
January	£17.50	£5.20	£24.00
February	£29.40	£8.40	£21.60
March	£27.30	£10.00	£14.40

1. How much was taken in February on pencils alone?

   _____

2. How much money was taken in January altogether?

   _____

3. What was the total taken for pen sales over the three-month period?

   _____

4. Last October the shop took twice as much money for pens as in

   February. How much was taken in October? _____

5. In November only half as much was taken for pad sales as in February.

   How much was taken in November? _____

6. Pencils cost 40p each. How many were sold in February? _____

7. In March, 39 pens were sold. How much were they each? _____

8. Only 10% of the takings are profit. How much profit was made on pads

   in March? _____

Extracting information:
length

A tile shop stocks the following sizes of tiles.

A
150mm by 20cm

B
30cm by 25cm

C
35cm by 0·4m

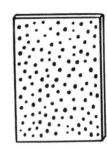

D
0·3m by 0·4m

E
20cm by 20cm

Patio slabs come in many shapes and sizes. The following table shows some examples.

	Haverley	Wentworth	Eastward
length	20cm	0·3m	35cm
width	20cm	0·2m	25cm
price	99p	£1.75	£1.99

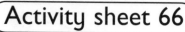

Extracting information:
length

Name

A tile shop stocks the following sizes of tiles.

A
150mm by 20cm

B
25cm by 25cm

C
30cm by 0·4m

1. What is the length of the longest side of tile A? _____

2. How wide is tile C in metres? _____

3. What is the perimeter of tile A in centimetres? _____

4. What is the perimeter of tile C in centimetres? _____

5. If I put 5 of tile C side by side (widthways) what length of wall in
    metres have I covered? _____

6. My wall is 2 metres tall. How many of
    tile A will I need to cover the wall
    from floor to ceiling? _____

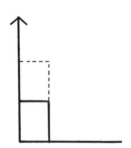

7. What is the area of tile C in square
    centimetres? _____

8. How many of tile B would be
    needed to cover an area
    1m by 2m? _____

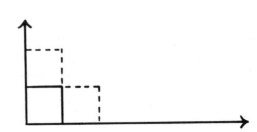

Extracting information:
length

Name _____

A tile shop stocks the following sizes of tiles.

A
160mm by 25cm

B
0·2m by 30cm

C
40cm by 0·4m

1. What is the length of the longest side of tile B? _____

2. How tall is tile A in metres? _____

3. What is the perimeter of tile C in centimetres? _____

4. What is the perimeter of tile A in centimetres? _____

5. If I put 7 of tile C side by side what length of wall in metres have I

    covered? _____

6. My wall is 2·1 metres tall. How many of tile B will I need

    to cover the wall from floor to ceiling? _____

7. What is the area of tile B? _____

8. Can I tile an area 2m by 3m using tile C

    without having to cut any tiles? _____

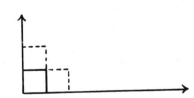

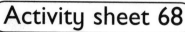

Extracting information:
length

Name

A tile shop stocks the following sizes of tiles.

A
150mm by 15cm

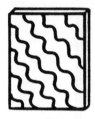

B
0·2m by 25cm

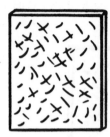

C
0·25m by 30cm

1. What is the length of the longest side of tile B? _____

2. How wide is tile C in centimetres? _____

3. What is the perimeter of tile A in centimetres? _____

4. What is the perimeter of tile C in centimetres? _____

5. If I put 9 of tile C side by side (widthways) what length of wall in

   metres have I covered? _____

6. The bath panel is 75cm from bottom to top.

   How many of tile A will I need to go from

   bottom to top? _____

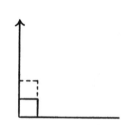

7. What is the area of tile C? _____

8. How many of tile B would be needed to cover

   an area 1m by 2m? _____

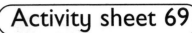
Extracting information:
length

Name _____

Patio slabs come in many shapes and sizes. The following table shows examples.

	Gloucester	Worcester	Evesham
length	18cm	0·3m	30cm
width	18cm	0·2m	15cm
price	99p	£2.50	£1.99

1. How wide in centimetres is a Worcester slab? _____

2. What is the perimeter of an Evesham slab? _____

3. What is the area of a Gloucester slab? _____

4. How much would 15 Gloucester slabs cost? _____

5. Ian needs 25 Gloucester slabs along the longest side of his patio. How

   long is his patio? _____

6. How many Worcester slabs will be needed

   across the width of this patio? _____

   How many will be needed along the

   length? _____

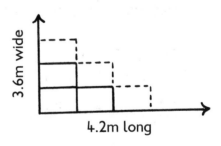

3.6m wide

4.2m long

   How much will it cost to buy slabs for the whole patio? _____

7. Betty lays her path using Evesham slabs in

   this design. How many slabs will she need

   to lay a path 4·5m long? _____

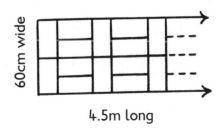

60cm wide

4.5m long

Extracting information:
length

Name _____

Patio slabs come in many shapes and sizes. The following table shows a sample.

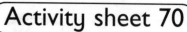

	Hampton	Windsor	Everley
length	25cm	0·4m	30cm
width	25cm	0·2m	20cm
price	99p	£2.20	£1.49

1. How wide in centimetres is a Windsor slab? _____

2. What is the perimeter of an Everley slab? _____

3. What is the area of a Hampton slab? _____

4. How much would 45 Hampton slabs cost? _____

5. Ian needs 18 Hampton slabs along the longest side of his patio.

   How long in metres is his patio? _____

6. How many Windsor slabs will be needed

   across the width of this patio? _____

   How many will be needed along the

   length? _____

   How much will it cost to buy slabs for

   the whole patio? _____

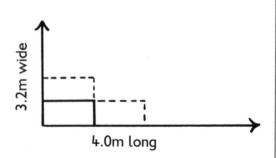

7. Betty lays her path using Everley slabs in

   this design. How many slabs will she

   need to lay a path 5m long? _____

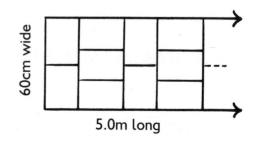

Extracting information:
mass

The bar chart shows the sales, in kilograms, of various fruit and vegetables.

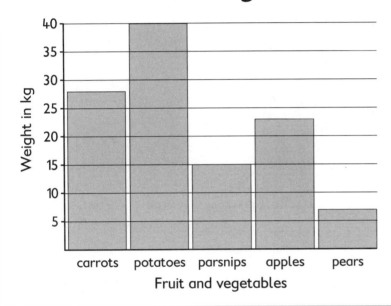

Weight in kg

carrots   potatoes   parsnips   apples   pears

Fruit and vegetables

Recipe for Lemon Shorties

for the dough:
- 250g plain flour
- 100g castor sugar
- 150g butter
- 2 egg yolks

for the filling:
- 25g butter
- 300ml single cream
- 25g plain flour
- 50g castor sugar
- 2 egg yolks
- grated rind of 1 lemon

Extracting information:
mass

Name

The bar chart shows the amount of sales, in kilograms, of various fruit and vegetables.

1. What is the weight of parsnips sold? _____

2. What was the combined weight of apples and carrots sold? _____

3. The following day 10% more apples were sold. How much more was that? _____

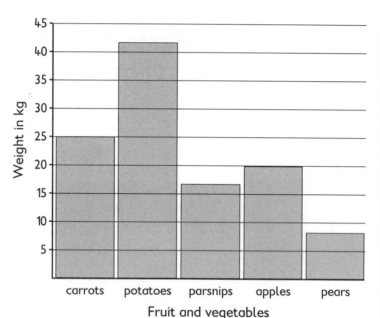

4. A local restaurant bought 50% of the carrots. What weight of carrots did the restaurant have? _____

5. Potatoes were sold in ready packed bags weighing 2·5kg each. If 10kg were sold how many bags were bought? _____

6. At the end of the day, two people bought more apples. The first bought 750g, the second bought 900g. What was the new total weight for apples? _____

7. If carrots were 40p per kilogram, how much money was taken for carrots alone? _____

8. If 6kg of the apples were sold in small ready packed bags and 12 bags were sold, how heavy was each bag? _____

Extracting information:
mass

Name _____

The bar chart shows the amount of sales, in kilograms, of various fruit and vegetables.

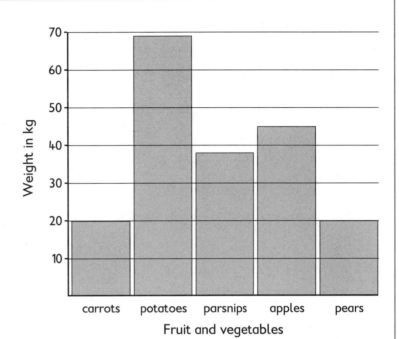

1. What is the weight of potatoes sold?

   _____

2. What is the combined weight of apples and carrots sold? _____

3. The following day 50% more apples were sold. Estimate the increase in kilograms of apples that were sold. _____

4. Mrs. Brown bought 20% of the total sale of pears. What weight of pears did she buy? _____

5. If 15kg of potatoes were sold in ready packed bags weighing 1·5kg each, how many were sold? _____

6. At the end of the day, two people bought more carrots. The first bought 550g, the second bought 700g. What was the new total weight for carrots? _____

7. If pears cost 85p per kilogram, how much money was taken for pears alone? _____

8. If 10kg of apples were sold in 8 ready packed bags, how heavy was each bag? _____

Extracting information:
mass

Name _____

The bar chart shows the amount of sales, in kilograms, of various fruit and vegetables.

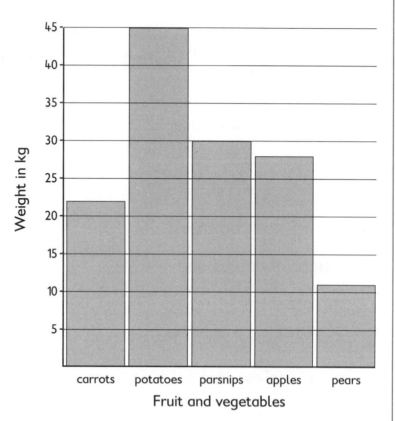

1. What is the weight of

    apples sold? _____

2. What was the combined

    weight of potatoes and

    parsnips sold? _____

3. The following day 10%

    more parsnips were sold.

    How much more was

    that? _____

4. A local restaurant bought

    50% of the carrots that were sold. What was the weight of carrots sold to

    the restaurant? _____

5. If 6kg of pears were sold in ready packed bags each weighing 500g, how

    many bags were sold? _____

6. At the end of the day, two people bought more parsnips. The first bought

    1.2kg, the second bought 900g. What was the new total weight for parsnips?

    _____

7. If potatoes cost 20p per kilogram, how much money was taken for potatoes

    alone? _____

8. If 12kg of apples were sold in 8 ready packed bags, how heavy was each

    bag? _____

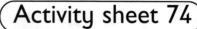

Extracting information:
mass

Name _____

Here are two recipes:

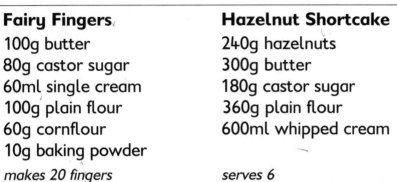

Fairy Fingers	**Hazelnut Shortcake**
100g butter	240g hazelnuts
80g castor sugar	300g butter
60ml single cream	180g castor sugar
100g plain flour	360g plain flour
60g cornflour	600ml whipped cream
10g baking powder	
makes 20 fingers	*serves 6*

1. How much plain flour is needed to make 20 Fairy Fingers? _____

2. How much butter would be needed to make 12 Hazelnut Shortcakes?

    _____

3. Rachel buys 1·2kg of hazelnuts. How much is left after making

    shortcake? _____

4. Rachel's packet of butter weighs half a kilogram. How much butter is

    left after making shortcake? _____

5. How many batches of Fairy Fingers can be made from a 250g bag of

    sugar? _____

6. How many batches of shortcakes can be made from a 1·5kg bag of

    flour? _____

7. How much cornflour would be needed in a recipe for only 5 Fairy

    Fingers? _____

8. Complete the Hazelnut Shortcake recipe to serve 9.
    hazelnuts _____
    butter _____
    castor sugar _____
    plain flour _____
    whipped cream _____

Extracting information:
mass

Name _____

Here are two recipes:

Cheesecake Mix	**Caramel Shortbread**
300g crushed biscuits	175g plain flour
150g castor sugar	50g castor sugar
150g melted butter	175g butter
	50g brown sugar
makes 2 bases	*makes 20 shortbreads*

1. How much plain flour is needed to make 20 shortbreads? _____

2. How much butter would be needed to make 4 cheesecake bases? _____

3. Terry buys a 2kg bag of sugar. How much is left after making the

   cheesecake mix? _____

4. Terry's packet of butter weighs three quarters of a kilogram. How much

   butter is left after making shortbread? _____

5. How many batches of cheesecake mix can be made from a 2kg bag of

   sugar? _____

6. How many batches of shortbread can be made from a 1kg bag of flour?

   _____

7. How much brown sugar would be needed for 30 shortbreads? _____

8. Complete this recipe for 5 cheesecake bases.

   crushed biscuits _____

   castor sugar _____

   melted butter _____

Extracting information:
capacity

Shown here are the capacities of some containers.

700ml

350ml

25ml

4·5l

40l

The table shows some information about drinks at a burger bar.

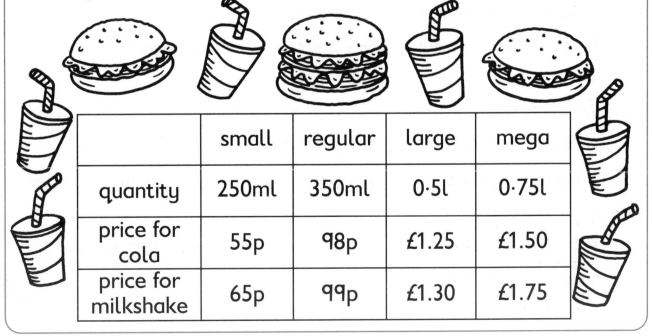

	small	regular	large	mega
quantity	250ml	350ml	0·5l	0·75l
price for cola	55p	98p	£1.25	£1.50
price for milkshake	65p	99p	£1.30	£1.75

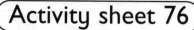

Extracting information:
capacity

Name _____

Shown here are the capacities of various containers.

750ml

300ml

25ml

5·5l

40l

1. Neil measures out 2 jugs full of milk. How many litres of milk has he measured out? _____

2. How many cups can be filled from 2 jugs? _____

3. If 3 egg cups of cordial are poured into a cup, how much water must be added to fill the cup? _____

4. How much water would 5 buckets hold? _____

5. On the farm, 2 and a half water butts are filled with rainwater. How much rainwater is in the butts? _____

6. Eric spills 900ml of water from a full bucket he is carrying. How much water is left in the bucket? _____

7. If 6 jugs of water are poured into the bucket, how many litres of water are in the bucket? _____

8. If 5 children share a jug of squash equally, how much do they each have? _____

Extracting information:
capacity

Name

Shown here are the capacities of various containers.

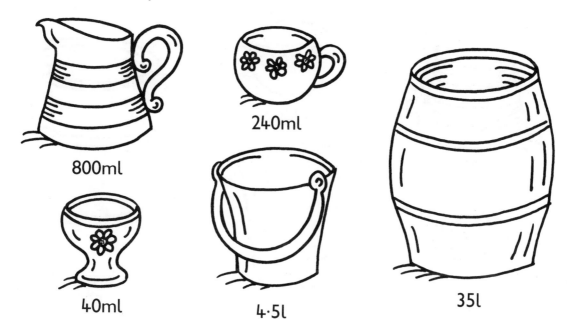

800ml

240ml

40ml

4·5l

35l

1. How many egg cups can be filled from 2 cups of water? _____

2. Jill measures out 2 jugs full of milk. How many litres of milk has she measured out? _____

3. If 2 egg cups of cordial are poured into a cup, how much water must be added to fill the cup? _____

4. On the farm 7 water butts are filled with rainwater. How much rainwater is in the butts? _____

5. How much water would 4 buckets hold? _____

6. Eddie spills 800ml of water from a full bucket as he carries it. How much water is left in the bucket? _____

7. If 5 children share 2 jugs of squash equally, how much do they each have? _____

8. If 20 jugs of water are poured into the water butt, how many litres of water are in the butt? _____

Extracting information:
capacity

Name _____

Shown here are the capacities of various containers.

900ml

200ml

20ml

6·5l

50l

1. Ken measures out 3 jugs full of milk. How many litres of milk has he measured out? _____

2. How many cups can be filled from 2 jugs? _____

3. If 3 egg cups of cordial are poured into a cup, how much water must be added to fill the cup? _____

4. How much water would 6 buckets hold? _____

5. On the farm 3 and a half water butts are filled with rainwater. How much rainwater is in the butts? _____

6. Becky spills 1200ml of water from a full bucket she is carrying. How much water is left in the bucket? _____

7. If 7 jugs of water are poured into the bucket, how many litres of water are in the bucket? _____

8. If 6 children share a jug of squash equally, how much do they each have? _____

Extracting information:
capacity

Name _____

The table shows some information about drinks at a burger bar.

	small	regular	large	mega
quantity	200ml	350ml	0·5l	0·7l
price for cola	58p	98p	£1.40	£1.75
price for milkshake	60p	99p	£1.50	£2.00

1. How much does a regular drink of cola cost? _____

2. How many millilitres of milkshake are in a large drink? _____

3. If Sally buys 3 regular colas how many litres of cola has she bought? _____

4. Billy only drinks three quarters of his small milkshake. How much has he drunk? _____

5. Megan leaves 20% of her regular cola. How much does she leave? _____

6. Don buys 3 regular shakes and 2 mega colas. How much change does he get from £10? _____

7. Which is the cheaper way to buy a litre of cola, 5 small or 2 large drinks? _____

8. How many Mega colas can be poured from a 25 litre barrel? _____

Extracting information:
capacity

Name

The table shows some information about drinks at a burger bar.

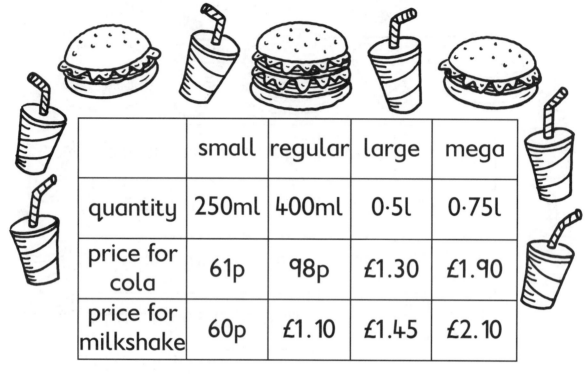

	small	regular	large	mega
quantity	250ml	400ml	0·5l	0·75l
price for cola	61p	98p	£1.30	£1.90
price for milkshake	60p	£1.10	£1.45	£2.10

1. How much does a large drink of cola cost? _____

2. How many millilitres of milkshake are in a mega drink? _____

3. If Malcolm buys 4 regular colas how many litres of cola has he bought? _____

4. Terry only drinks three fifths of his mega milkshake. How much has he drunk? _____

5. Megan leaves 30% of her regular cola. How much does she leave? _____

6. Tracey buys 4 small colas and 3 large shakes. How much change does she get from £10? _____

7. Which is the cheaper way to buy a litre of cola, 4 small or 2 large drinks? _____

8. How many mega colas can be poured from a 20 litre barrel? _____

Extracting information:
time

This notice is displayed in a shop window.

	morning	afternoon
Mon-Fri	7.30-12.00	1.00-6.30
Sat	8.00-12.00	1.30-5.00
Sun	closed	1.00-4.30

These are opening times at an athletics training track.

	Opening times		
	am		pm
Monday	track closed		
Tuesday	9.30	to	5.30
Wednesday	9.30	to	6.30
Thursday	track closed		
Friday	9.00	to	8.00
Saturday	9.30	to	8.00
Sunday	9.30	to	6.30

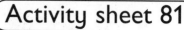

Extracting information:
time

Name _____

This notice is displayed in a shop window.

	morning	afternoon
Mon-Fri	8.30-12.00	1.30-6.00
Sat	9.00-12.00	1.30-5.30
Sun	closed	2.00-4.00

1. What time does the shop open on Monday morning? _____

2. What time does the shop open on Sunday? _____

3. What time does the shop close on Wednesday afternoon? _____

4. If Ben arrives at the shop at 8.45 a.m. on Tuesday morning, will the

   shop be open? _____

5. Angela wants to pop in to the shop on her way home on Saturday

   afternoon. By what time must she get there? _____

6. Jamaine arrives at the shop at five to one on a Thursday. How long

   must he wait for the shop to open? _____

7. On Tuesday Molly, the shopkeeper, was having a bad day! She couldn't

   wait to close the shop at 3.45 p.m. How much longer did she have to

   work? _____

8. Last week Rob worked all day Monday and Tuesday, and then

   Saturday morning at the shop. How many hours did he work? (Include

   lunchtime as working.) _____

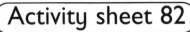

Extracting information:
time

Name _____

This notice is displayed in a shop window.

		Closed for lunch
Mon-Thurs	08:00-17:30	13:00-14:00
Fri & Sat	08:30-18:30	open all day
Sun	closed all day	

1. What time does the shop open on Monday morning? _____

2. What time does the shop open on Friday? _____

3. What time does the shop close on Saturday? _____

4. If Ben arrives at the shop at 8.45 a.m. on Friday morning, will the shop
   be open? _____

5. Sarah wants to call in before the shop closes for lunch on Wednesday.
   By what time must she get there? _____

6. Ally leaves the shop as it closes on Thursday afternoon and takes three
   quarters of an hour to get home. At what time does she arrive home?
   _____

7. On Monday Molly, the shopkeeper, was hungry by 11.20 a.m. How
   long did she have to wait until lunchtime? _____

8. This week Rob only worked Monday and Tuesday afternoons at the
   shop. How many hours did he work? _____

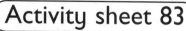

Extracting information:
time

Name _____

This notice is displayed in a shop window.

	morning	afternoon
Mon-Fri	08:00-12:00	13:00-18:30
Sat	07:30-12:00	13:30-18:00
Sun	11:00-13:00	closed

1. What time does the shop open on Thursday morning? _____

2. What time does the shop open on Saturday morning? _____

3. What time does the shop close on Wednesday afternoon? _____

4. If Sarah arrives at the shop on Tuesday at 07:50 will it be open?

    _____

5. Mary arrives at the shop to fill shelves at 06:55 on Saturday. How long does she have before it is time to open the shop? _____

6. Danny leaves the shop as it closes on Monday and takes 40 minutes to get home. At what time does he arrive home? _____

7. On Wednesday afternoon Molly, the shopkeeper, was tired by 20 to 5. How much longer did she have to work? _____

8. This week Rob worked all day Monday, Thursday morning and all day Saturday. How many hours did he work? (Include lunchtime as working.) _____

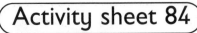

Extracting information:
time

Name _____

These are opening times at an athletics training track.

	am		pm
Monday		track closed	
Tuesday	10.30	to	5.30
Wednesday	10.30	to	6.00
Thursday		track closed	
Friday	9.00	to	8.30
Saturday	8.30	to	9.00
Sunday	8.30	to	4.30

1. How many hours is the track open on a Wednesday? _____

2. Which day has the latest closing time? _____

3. Robby arrives at the track at 19:40 on Friday. How many minutes is it before the track closes? _____

4. Elly goes to the track every day it is open and trains for 40 minutes. How many hours training is that each week? _____

5. Cheryl's bus arrived at the track 17 minutes before the track opened on Tuesday. What time did her bus arrive? _____

6. At the start of the season Eric ran 400m in 58 seconds. At his personal best he took 10% off this time. What was his personal best? _____

7. Derek ran 400m in 59 seconds. His little brother took 83 seconds. Hamid's best time was exactly halfway between them. What time did Hamid run? _____

8. Michelle was at the track for 2 and a half hours. She spent a fifth of her time talking to her coach and a third of it chatting and changing. How long did she train for? _____

Extracting information:
time

Name

These are opening times at an athletics training track.

	am		pm
Monday	10.00	to	5.00
Tuesday	10.00	to	5.30
Wednesday		track closed	
Thursday	10.30	to	6.00
Friday	10.00	to	8.30
Saturday	8.00	to	9.30
Sunday	8.00	to	4.30

1. How many hours is the track open on a Friday? _____

2. Which day has the latest opening time? _____

3. Ravi arrives at the track at 3.25p.m. on Sunday. How many minutes is it before the track closes? _____

4. Paul goes to the track every day it is open and trains for 35 minutes. How many hours training is that each week? _____

5. Jo's bus left the track 19 minutes after the track closed on Tuesday. What time did her bus leave? _____

6. At the start of the season Charlie ran 200m in 32 seconds. At his personal best he took 10% off this time. What was his personal best?

   _____

7. Eddy ran 400m in 62 seconds. His little brother took 84 seconds. Ian's best time was exactly halfway between them. What time did Ian run?

   _____

8. Camilla was at the track for 1 and a half hours. She spent a fifth of her time talking to her coach and a third of it chatting and changing. How long did she train for? _____

Extracting information:
number

A small sports shop sells trainers, sweatshirts and sports bags. This chart shows how many of each were sold in February.

Items sold in February

⊕ is 4 pairs of trainers   ▦ is 4 sweatshirts   ⊠ is 4 bags

trainers	⊕ ⊕ ⊕ ⊕ ⊕
sweatshirts	▦ ▦ ▦
bags	⊠ ⊠ ⊠ ⊠

This bar graph shows the attendance at an ice rink for 5 consecutive Saturdays.

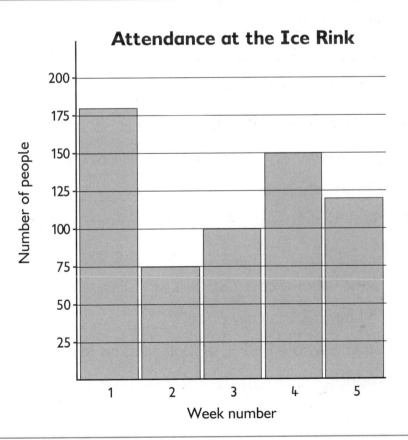

Attendance at the Ice Rink

Extracting information:
number

Name

A small sports shop sells trainers, sweatshirts and sports bags. This chart shows how many of each were sold in September.

Items sold in September

is 4 pairs of trainers   is 4 bags   is 4 sweatshirts

trainers	
sweatshirts	
bags	

1. How many pairs of trainers were sold in September? _____

2. The manager had hoped to sell 20 sweatshirts. He was short of his target – by how many? _____

3. The shop had 20 bags at the beginning of September. How many of these bags did the shop have left at the end of September? _____

4. In August the shop sold half as many sweatshirts as it did in September. How many sweatshirts did the shop sell in August? _____

5. In December the shop sold twice as many trainers. How many trainers did the shop sell in December? _____

6. Sweatshirts cost £9 each. How much money was taken for sweatshirts?

    _____

7. Bags usually cost £8.50 but in December they were reduced by 10%. What was the new price? _____

8. In the whole year the shop sold an average of 15 pairs of trainers a month. What was the total number of pairs of trainers sold in the year?

    _____

Extracting information:
number

Name _____

A small sweet shop sells bars of chocolate, Miracles, Hercules and Saturn. This chart shows how many of each they sold in May.

Items sold in May

○ is 5 Miracle bars   ▭ is 5 Hercules bars   ⬠ is 5 Saturn bars

Miracle bars	○ ○ ○ ○ ◔
Hercules bars	▭ ▭ ▭ ▭
Saturn bars	⬠ ⬠ ⬠

1. How many Saturn bars were sold in May? _____

2. How many more Miracle bars than Hercules bars were sold? _____

3. The shop had 36 Miracle bars at the beginning of May. How many of these bars did the shop have left at the end of May? _____

4. In April the shop only sold half as many Hercules bars. How many Hercules bars did the shop sell in April? _____

5. In July the shop sold 4 times as many Saturn bars. How many Saturn bars did the shop sell in July? _____

6. Hercules bars cost 23p each. How much money was taken for Hercules bars? _____

7. Miracle bars usually cost 32p but in August they were reduced by 25%. What was the new price? _____

8. In the whole year the shop sold an average of 26 Saturn bars a month. What was the total number of Saturn bars sold in the year? _____

Extracting information:
number

Name

A small music shop sells clarinets, flutes and trumpets. This chart shows how many of each they sold in April.

Items sold in April

is 4 clarinets   is 4 flutes   is 4 trumpets

clarinets	
flutes	
trumpets	

1. How many clarinets were sold in April? _____

2. The manager had hoped to sell 25 trumpets. How many short of his target was he? _____

3. The shop had 20 clarinets at the beginning of April. How many of these clarinets did the shop have left at the end of April? _____

4. In December the shop only sold half as many flutes. How many flutes did the shop sell in December? _____

5. In May the shop sold 3 times as many trumpets. How many trumpets did the shop sell in May? _____

6. Flutes cost £399 each. How much money was taken for flutes?

    _____

7. Clarinets usually cost £485.50 but in December they were reduced by 10%. By how much were they reduced? _____

8. In the next four months the shop sold a total of 72 clarinets. If they sold the same number each month, how many did they sell each month? _____

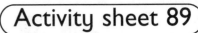

Extracting information:
number

Name _____

This bar graph shows the attendance at a cinema for 5 consecutive Saturdays.

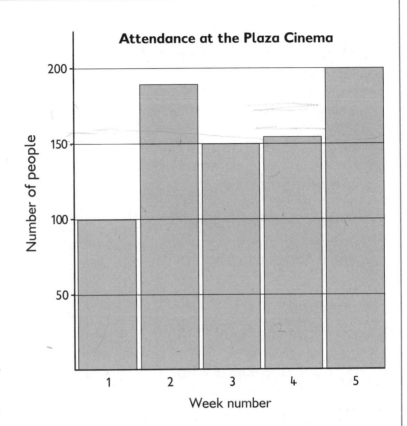

Attendance at the Plaza Cinema

Number of people

Week number

1. Estimate the number of people that attended on the fourth Saturday

    _____

2. Which two Saturdays were the most popular?

    _____

3. Estimate, to the nearest 100, the total number of people who went to the cinema on the five Saturdays. _____

4. If tickets are £3.25, how much money did the cinema take on the third Saturday? _____

5. If 20% of the people who attended on the fourth Saturday had popcorn, approximately how many people had popcorn? _____

6. Of the 135 people who attended the cinema on the sixth Saturday, 40% were school children. How many school children attended the cinema?

    _____

7. The film started showing at 19:45 and lasted 1 hour 50 minutes. At what time did it end? _____

8. If each row can seat 15 people how many rows were needed on the fifth Saturday? _____

Extracting information:
number

Name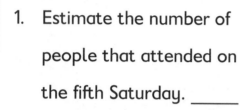

This bar graph shows the attendance at an ice rink for 5 consecutive Saturdays.

1. Estimate the number of people that attended on the fifth Saturday. _____

2. Which two Saturdays were the most popular?

    _____

3. Estimate the total number of people who went to the ice rink on the five Saturdays.

    _____

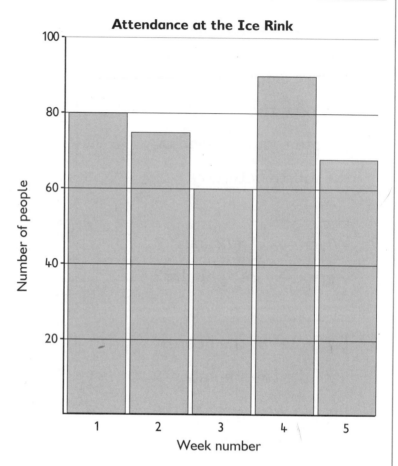

Attendance at the Ice Rink

Number of people (y-axis: 20, 40, 60, 80, 100)

Week number (x-axis: 1, 2, 3, 4, 5)

4. If tickets are £2.65, how much money did the Ice Rink take on the fourth Saturday? _____

5. If 20% of the people who attended on the third Saturday had their own boots, how many people had their own boots? _____

6. On the sixth Saturday 65 people attended, 60% of whom were school children. How many school children attended? _____

7. The disco skating started at 18:20 and lasted 1 and three-quarter hours. At what time did it end? _____

8. At the ice hockey match on Sunday there were 395 spectators. If each row can seat 15 people how many rows were filled? _____

Mental arithmetic:
practice test

For the first group of questions you will have five seconds to work out the answer and write it down.

1. Multiply 73 by 10.
2. What is 1543 to the nearest hundred?
3. What is 64 divided by 8?
4. Write a half as a percentage.
5. Write the number three thousand and four in figures.
6. Change 5 and a half kilograms into grams.
7. What is 7 multiplied by 6?
8. Write quarter to five in the evening as it would appear on a digital watch.

For the next group of questions you will have ten seconds to work out the answer and write it down.

9. The side of a square is 6 centimetres. What is the area of the square?
10. I take 2 hours and 20 minutes to travel home from my holiday. I set out at 4.50 p.m. At what time do I get home?
11. Look at the numbers on your sheet. What is the mode of the numbers?
12. What temperature is 5°C warmer than −2°C?
13. What is 3·4 multiplied by 100?
14. What is 25% of £80?
15. On your sheet is a scale. Estimate the number shown by the arrow.
16. Look at the shape on your sheet. What is it called?
17. Subtract 65 from 134.
18. How many eights in 480?
19. What is the product of 70 and 6?
20. Jack saves £1.50 a week. How much will he have saved in 8 weeks?

For the next group of questions you will have fifteen seconds to work out the answer and write it down.

21. I think of a number and add 17. The answer is 32. What was the number?
22. Start with 6. Multiply it by 8 and add 12. What is the answer?
23. How many tents will be needed for 65 children if 9 can sleep in each tent?
24. In a class of 32 children, 25% are girls. How many girls is that?
25. The sides of a rectangle are 3·5cm and 6cm. What is the perimeter?

Mental arithmetic:
practice test

Name

Time 5 seconds

1	

2	

3	

4	

5	

6		g	5½kg

7	

8	

Time 10 seconds

9	

10	

11		7, 12, 12, 11, 14

12	

13	

14		25%	80

15		0 ———↓——— 100

16		

17	

18	

19	

20		£1.50	8

Time 15 seconds

21	

22	

23		65	9

24		32	25%

25		3·5cm	6cm

Test questions:

Name _____

1. Write in the missing numbers.

   134 + ____ = 211   ____ + 87 = 156

   141 − ____ = 88   ____ − 113 = 76

2. Here is a triangle.

   What is the perimeter?

   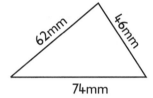

   62mm   46mm   74mm

3. Naomi buys these three packets of sweets.

   Lemon bonbons 75p      Mints 82p      Humbugs 89p

   What is the total cost of the

   three packets?

   Mark buys 2 packets of mints.

   How much change does he

   get from £5?

Test questions:

Name

4. Here are the times of some television programmes.

Channel 1
19:00	News
19:30	Comedy
20:00	Soap Opera
20:35	Sport
21:10	Film
22:55	Drama

Channel 2
19:00	News
19:30	Film
21:15	Quiz Show
21:50	Late News
22:05	Weather
22:10	Sport

What is showing on Channel 1 at ten minutes to nine?

How long does the film on Channel 1 last?

Alex watches the Soap Opera on Channel 1. He then turns over to watch the end of the film on Channel 2. How much of the film has he missed?

5. Fill in the missing numbers.

$7 \times \underline{\hspace{1cm}} = 63$ $\underline{\hspace{1cm}} \times 4 = 68$

$42 \div \underline{\hspace{1cm}} = 6$ $\underline{\hspace{1cm}} \div 6 = 14$

6. Floppy disks are sold in packs of 8. A company bought 184 disks. How many packs did they buy?

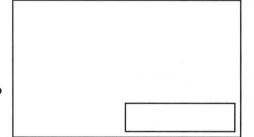

Test questions:

Name

7. A camping shop sold 15 tents, 26 backpacks and 29 sleeping bags. The following month 3 times as many backpacks were sold. How many were sold?

8. Last year 469 people came to the school play. This year there was an increase of 74. How many people came to the school play this year?

9. Ravi and Helen are playing darts. Their target number is 301. So far Ravi has scored 78, 47 and 62. What is the sum of Ravi's scores so far?

Helen has scored 39, 86 and 93. How much does she need to reach the target number?

10. This bag holds 3.5kg of potatoes. Jerry uses 850g for dinner. What weight of potatoes is left?

Test questions:

Name _____

1. Write in the missing numbers.

   ___ × 6 = 54   ___ ÷ 7 = 8

   ___ × 8 = 192   ___ ÷ 6 = 17

2. This table shows the numbers of children who played netball, football or hockey at a sports camp.

month / sport	April	May	June
Netball	27	62	59
Football	70	43	64
Hockey	34	60	58

   How many children played netball in April, May and June altogether?

   How many more children played football in April than in May?

   In July 10% more children played hockey than in May. How many more children played hockey in July?

3. Billy thinks of a number, adds 15 and divides by 6. The answer is 5. What was his number?

Test questions:

Name

4. Here are some of the items for sale in a tack shop.

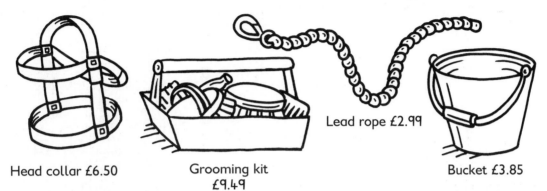

Head collar £6.50   Grooming kit   Lead rope £2.99   Bucket £3.85
                              £9.49

Graham buys a bucket and a
grooming kit. How much do
they cost him?

Wendy buys three lead ropes.
How much change does she
get from £10?

In one week the shop sells
8 buckets. How much money
do they take for buckets
that week?

5. Write in the missing numbers.

    ___ + 107 = 259   314 – ___ = 82

    69 + ___ = 243   ___ – 74 = 123

6. A piano teacher gives 25 lessons
    a week. How many lessons does
    she teach in 15 weeks?

Test questions:

Name

7. This bar chart shows the money raised for charity by 5 different charity groups.

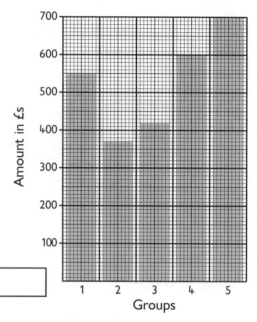

What was the amount raised by Group 2?

How much more money does Group 3 need to raise to reach their target of £1000?

In the following two months Group 4 raises another 30% of their total so far. How much do they raise in those two months?

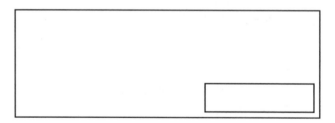

8. Here are some containers.

mug 350ml

jug 1 litre

glass 225ml

A glass is filled from a jug full of water. How much water is left in the jug?

Fran wants to fill 3 mugs from a jug full of milk. Has she enough milk to fill 3 mugs?

Test questions:

Name

1. Write in what the missing numbers could be.

    Both numbers have 3 digits:
    ___ + ___ + 240 = 1000

    Two numbers more than 100:
    ___ − ___ = 301

    Both numbers are less than 20:
    ___ × ___ = 270

    Two numbers between 14 and 25:
    315 ÷ ___ = ___

2. A sack of pony cubes costs £5.65. Julian's ponies eat a sack of cubes each week. How much does it cost him to feed the ponies for a year?

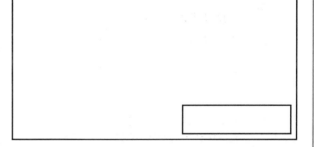

3. Erica put all her 50 pence pieces in a jar. At the end of the year she counted them and found she had 57 coins. How much money did she have?

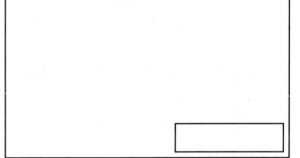

Test questions:

Name

4. Here is a recipe for biscuits.
    150g plain flour
    70g castor sugar
    175g butter
    50g brown sugar

Harry had a 1·5kg bag of flour. How much flour does he have left after making the biscuits?

He has 1kg of butter. How many batches of the biscuits could he make before he runs out of butter?

This recipe makes 10 large biscuits. How much castor sugar would be needed in a recipe for 15 biscuits?

5. At last week's football match there were forty thousand seven hundred and two fans. Write the number of fans in figures.

6. Bottles of lemonade come in crates of 24. A barman needed 270 bottles for a party. How many crates must he buy?

Test questions:

Name

7. Eleanor digs a rectangular fish pond 1·2m by 0·8m.
   She wants to edge around it with 20cm bricks.

   0·8m

   1·2m

   How many bricks does she need?

8. A small music shop sells cornets, oboes and French horns. This chart shows how many of each they sold in March.

   Items sold in March

   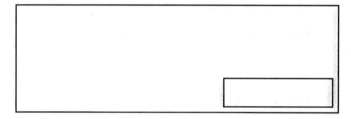

   is 4 cornets   is 4 oboes   is 4 French horns

cornets				
oboes				
French horns				

   How many cornets were sold?

   If French horns were £615.99 each, how much money was taken for French horns alone?

   The following month 20% more cornets were sold. How many more cornets were sold?

Test questions:

Name

1. Write in the missing numbers.

    ___ + 240 + 320 = 700   900 − 230 − ____ = 250

    5 × 7 × ___ = 175   4 × 6 × ___ = 192

2. The school tuck shop sells 123 bars of chocolate for 38p each. How much money did they take?

3. A secondhand car had 78439 miles on the clock. The new owner increased the mileage by 740 miles a month. How many miles had the car travelled a year later?

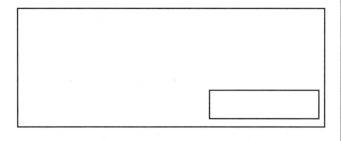

4. This bar chart shows the attendance at a local youth club for 5 consecutive weeks.

    What was the total number that attended the youth club in weeks 3 and 4.

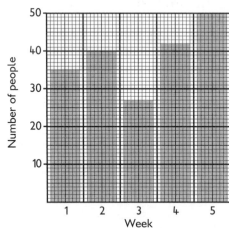

Attendance at the youth club

    Of those that attended in week 2, 30% were girls. How many were girls?

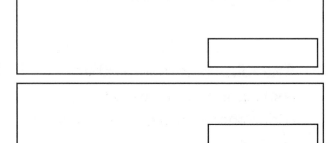

    In week 6, £27.20 was taken in entry fees. There were 32 at the youth club. How much is the entry fee?

Test questions:

Name

5. Sanjiv buys a plank of wood 2·4m long. He cuts pieces 65cm long from it. How many pieces 65cm long can he cut?

6. Here is a train timetable

	train A	train B	train C
Winchley	14:32	14:50	15:15
Drew	14:40	14:58	15:24
Charlthurst	14:56	15:15	15:31
Fordham	15:03	15:24	15:38

At what time does train B leave Winchley?

How long does it take train B to get from Winchley to Fordham?

Train C runs 25 minutes late. At what time does it arrive at Fordham?

7. Harry thinks of a number. He multiplies it by 17 and then subtracts 153. The answer is 153. What was Harry's number?

Test questions:

Name

8. Billy saves £34.60. Hannah saves £22.80. Fred's savings are exactly halfway between Billy and Hannah's savings. How much has Fred saved?

9. Here are some pictures.

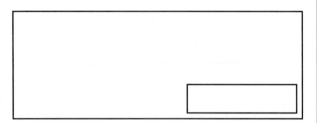

A 25cm by 30cm £156   **B** 20cm by 40cm £234   **C** 32cm by 32cm £264

The perimeter of the picture Ali buys is 1·2m. Which picture did Ali buy?

Ali pays for the picture in twelve equal monthly payments. How much does he pay each month?

10. A shop sells these clothes.
    shirt – £16.99
    trousers – £26.45
    jumper – £32.85

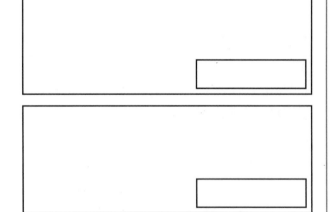

Neil buys 2 shirts, a pair of trousers and 2 jumpers. How much change does he get from £150?

Dave gets 20% off a pair of trousers. How much money does he get off?

Missing numbers: addition

Activity sheet 1 1) 7, 2) 8, 3) 8, 4) 15, 5) 17, 6) 16, 7) 14, 8) 16, 9) 26, 10) 26, 11) two numbers total 15, 12) two numbers total 24, 13) two numbers total 19, 14) two numbers total 38.

Activity sheet 2 1) 5, 2) 17, 3) 23, 4) 26, 5) 25, 6) 25, 7) 17, 8) 26, 9) 17, 10) 17, 11) two numbers total 19, 12) two numbers total 19, 13) two numbers total 28, 14) two numbers total 27.

Activity sheet 3 1) 11, 2) 14, 3) 22, 4) 15, 5) 36, 6) 15, 7) 16, 8) 27, 9) 38, 10) 36, 11) two numbers total 19, 12) two numbers total 33, 13) two numbers total 22, 14) two numbers total 35.

Activity sheet 4 1) 101, 2) 207, 3) 181, 4) 15, 5) 138, 6) 215, 7) 216, 8) 357, 9) 398, 10) 456, 11) two numbers total 189, 12) two numbers total 413, 13) two numbers total 224, 14) two numbers total 388.

Activity sheet 5 1) 108, 2) 211, 3) 177, 4) 35, 5) 189, 6) 239, 7) 413, 8) 519, 9) 437, 10) 1516, 11) two numbers total 213, 12) two numbers total 363, 13) two numbers total 397, 14) two numbers total 692.

Missing numbers: subtraction

Activity sheet 6 1) 18, 2) 27, 3) 135, 4) 57, 5) 179, 6) 113, 7) 220, 8) 35, 9) 152, 10) 57.

Activity sheet 7 1) 17, 2) 86, 3) 56, 4) 87, 5) 74, 6) 101, 7) 222, 8) 28, 9) 157, 10) 49.

Activity sheet 8 1) 15, 2) 39, 3) 69, 4) 77, 5) 45, 6) 165, 7) 213, 8) 182, 9) 44, 10) 239.

Activity sheet 9 1) 70, 2) 956, 3) 717, 4) 448, 5) 1039, 6) 1260, 7) 557, 8) 462, 9) 1727, 10) 1913, 11) and 12) there are many possible answers, 13) 300, 14) there are many possible answers, 15) 500.

Activity sheet 10 1) 213, 2) 285, 3) 339, 4) 362, 5) 407, 6) 1156, 7) 289, 8) 8394, 9) 3866, 10) 13 720, 11) and 12) there are many possible answers, 13) 530, 14) there are many possible answers, 15) 685.

Missing numbers: multiplication

Activity sheet 11 1) 7, 2) 6, 3) 5, 4) 8, 5) 6, 6) 9, 7) 9, 8) 9, 9) 9, 10) 7, 11) 17, 12) 17, 13) 26, 14) 36, 15) 19.

Activity sheet 12 1) 9, 2) 7, 3) 4, 4) 10, 5) 8, 6) 8, 7) 6, 8) 8, 9) 9, 10) 9, 11) 22, 12) 23, 13) 22, 14) 39, 15) 18.

Activity sheet 13 1) 7, 2) 8, 3) 6, 4) 7, 5) 7, 6) 7, 7) 4, 8) 4, 9) 5, 10) 8, 11) 43, 12) 42, 13) 27, 14) 34, 15) 24.

Activity sheet 14 1) 14, 2) 19, 3) 18, 4) 19, 5) 17, 6) 16, 7) 18, 8) 13, 9) 19, 10) 14, 11) 9×14 or 21×6, 12) 6×19, 13) 13×11, 14) 8×17, 15) 9×18.

Activity sheet 15 1) 17, 2) 18, 3) 21, 4) 17, 5) 22, 6) 16, 7) 14, 8) 22, 9) 26, 10) 19, 11) $3 \times 4 \times 5$, 12) $2 \times 9 \times 5$, 13) $7 \times 3 \times 5$, 14) $3 \times 4 \times 8$, 15) $3 \times 5 \times 9$, (there are other possible answers for 11 to 15).

Missing numbers: division

Activity sheet 16 1) 9, 2) 4, 3) 9, 4) 6, 5) 7, 6) 5, 7) 24, 8) 14, 9) 25, 10) 14, 11) 35, 12) 18, 13) 98, 14) 57, 15) 102.

Activity sheet 17 1) 7, 2) 9, 3) 8, 4) 7, 5) 9, 6) 9, 7) 13, 8) 15, 9) 23, 10) 17, 11) 24, 12) 28, 13) 90, 14) 126, 15) 136.

Activity sheet 18 1) 8, 2) 8, 3) 10, 4) 8, 5) 8, 6) 7, 7) 18, 8) 24, 9) 27, 10) 57, 11) 48, 12) 63, 13) 92, 14) 90, 15) 176.

Activity sheet 19 1) 16, 2) 324, 3) 13, 4) 19, 5) 192, 6) 22, 7) 289, 8) 19, 9) 22, 10) 357, 11) 17,16, 12) 21,22, 13) 19,21, 14) 23,18, 15) 19,17.

Activity sheet 20 1) 23, 2) 288, 3) 18, 4) 24, 5) 304, 6) 19, 7) 306, 8) 25, 9) 19, 10) 408 11) 18,24, 12) 23,19, 13) 16,21, 14) 22,19, 15) 13,19.

Missing numbers: mixed

Activity sheet 21 1) 57, 2) 46, 3) 55, 4) 9, 5) 72, 6) 6, 7) 76, 8) 192, 9) 6, 10) 7, 11) 26, 12) 32, 13) 229, 14) 177, 15) 114, 16) 301.

Activity sheet 22 1) 8, 2) 28, 3) 69, 4) 79, 5) 63, 6) 4, 7) 51, 8) 27, 9) 7, 10) 309, 11) 52, 12) 28, 13) 15, 14) 226, 15) 186, 16) 417.

Activity sheet 23 1) 81, 2) 9, 3) 39, 4) 56, 5) 59, 6) 8, 7) 38, 8) 42, 9) 8, 10) 463, 11) 43, 12) 55, 13) 503, 14) 127, 15) 296, 16) 117.

Activity sheet 24 1) 347, 2) 387, 3) 52, 4) 45, 5) 543, 6) 1281, 7) 36, 8) 1176, 9) 39, 10) 51, 11) to 15) have many possible answers.

Activity sheet 25 1) 233, 2) 558, 3) 35, 4) 28, 5) 2152, 6) 825, 7) 51, 8) 1512, 9) 38, 10) 62, (11 to 15 have other possible answers) 11) 3,5,10, 12) 3,6,9, 13) 3,4,12, 14) 12,18 or 9,24, 15) 13,19.

Solving problems: vocabulary of add and subtract

Activity sheet 26 1) 25cm, 2) 262km, 3) 26, 4) £1.21, 5) 306, 6) 84cm, 7) £5, 8) 201cm, 9) 45g, 10) 1325ml.

Activity sheet 27 1) 1h 35m, 2) 65g, 3) £11.25, 4) 39, 5) 540, 6) £350, 7) 182, 8) 1h 10m, 9) £7.54, 10) 92.

Activity sheet 28 1) 28m, 2) 39, 3) 65, 4) 211km, 5) 38, 6) 67, 7) £42.39, 8) 325g, 9) 68, 10) 65.

Activity sheet 29 1) 544, 2) 2409km, 3) 433 miles, 4) 3·95kg, 5) 14421, 6) £1.65, 7) £13450, 8) 54748 miles, 9) £95450, 10) 77900.

Activity sheet 30 1) 33105, 2) 9741, 3) 5956km, 4) 3·5kg, 5) £8.94, 6) 306620km², 7) 2028km, 8) £445850, 9) 249981, 10) £590000.

Solving problems: vocabulary of multiply and divide

Activity sheet 31 1a) £11.25, 1b) £5, 2a) 1500g, 2b) 95g, 3a) £1.20, 3b) £10.80, 4a) 19cm, 4b) 119cm, 5a) 125ml, 5b) 700ml, 6a) 666 seconds, 6b) 71 seconds.

Activity sheet 32 1) 477, 2) 174, 3) 735, 4) 144, 5) 41, 6) 825 minutes, 7) 560, 8) 115ml, 9) 910cm, 10) 97m.

Activity sheet 33 1) 14, 2) 52, 3) 192, 4) 29, 5) £14.70, 6) £79.50, 7) 2548, 8) £40.25, 9) 29m, 10) 23.

Activity sheet 34 1) £8490, 2) £232.50, 3) £674.73, 4) 14085, 5) £19, 6) 2196, 7) 12·5cm, 8) 5640, 9) 1·275kg, 10) 6 seconds.

Activity sheet 35 1) 66, 2) 26, 3) 7, 4) 2891, 5) £24900, 6) £35.72, 7) 117·5cm, 8) 136, 9) £15.50, 10) 45·1cm².

Solving problems: single step

Activity sheet 36 1) 24, 2) 4, 3) £48.49, 4) 975ml, 5) 612m, 6) 19, 7) 87, 8) 98km, 9) 16, 10) 142.

Activity sheet 37 1) 450m, 2) 4, 3) 28, 4) 165mm, 5) £24.49, 6) 1720 miles, 7) 57, 8) 18, 9) 575g, 10) 18.

Activity sheet 38 1) 78, 2) 36, 3) £29.48, 4) 3090 litres, 5) 1380m, 6) 27, 7) 169, 8) 696, 9) 23, 10) 379.

Activity sheet 39 1) £225, 2) 14·48kg, 3) £3, 4) 374524km, 5) 1631·5m, 6) 6, 7) 227500 litres, 8) 68·25m, 9) 1·5g, 10) 35p.

Activity sheet 40 1) £32345, 2) £13.50, 3) £273, 4) 5·448kg, 5) 163·8 seconds, 6) 26, 7) 2405 miles, 8) 45p, 9) 47·11 seconds, 10) £101.25.

Solving problems: relevant information

Activity sheet 41 1) 3rd Sept, 2) 4, 3) £1.62, 4) 56, 5) £67.34, 6) 165g, 7) 16.

Activity sheet 42 1) 15p, 2) 22 seconds, 3) 5.05 p.m., 4) 144, 5) 6, 6) 85, 7) 181.

Activity sheet 43 1) £3.51, 2) 74km, 3) 1750ml, 4) £34, 5) 17:10, 6) 58, 7) 116.

Activity sheet 44 1) £96.49, 2) 470km, 3) £17.50, 4) 7439 miles, 5) £255.50, 6) 260 miles, 7) £171.50.

Activity sheet 45 1) 9p, 2) £42.25, 3) 6.35 p.m., 4) 45, 5) £7469, 6) £499.50, 7) 641 miles.

Solving problems: changing units

Activity sheet 46 1) 240cm, 3200g, 4·2cm, 276p, 5·6 litres, 3·5kg, 2) 250ml, 3) 750g, 4) 10cm, 5) £5.13, 6) 850g, 7) 9, 8) 1·25kg, 9) 3h 20min, 10) 152mm.

Activity sheet 47 1) 5cm, 7500ml, 370cm, £3.50, 8.5km, 55mm, 2) 100g, 3) 750m, 4) 250mm, 5) 480g, 6) 2375ml or 2·375 litres, 7) £7.33, 8) 10, 9) 140mm or 14cm, 10) 1h 40min.

Activity sheet 48 1) 855p, 7400g, 4·1kg, 320cm, 4·3 litres, 13·5cm, 2) 100mm, 3) 75cm, 4) 500ml, 5) £4.95, 6) 20, 7) 25, 8) 2375g or 2·375kg, 9) 2h 20min, 10) 207mm².

Activity sheet 49 1) 78cm, 2) 6·27kg, 3) 12, 4) 15, 5) 8, 6) 5 minutes, 7) 52·5cm, 8) £18.20, 9) 320ml, 10) 5 seconds.

Activity sheet 50 1) 88cm, 2) 1268m, 3) 8, 4) 8·25m, 5) 24, 6) £3.32, 7) 35·5cm, 8) £19.24, 9) 2·7 litres, 10) 3 seconds.

Solving problems: multi–step

Activity sheet 51 1) £1.65, 2) £1.50, 3) 0·6m, 4) 20:55, 5) £2.40, 6) 216, 7) 81, 8) 12, 9) 9, 10) 21.

Activity sheet 52 1) 11:50, 2) £3, 3) 1·2m,
4) £1.50, 5) 225g, 6) 22, 7) 58, 8) 31 seconds,
9) 7, 10) 14.

Activity sheet 53 1) £2.02, 2) 250g, 3) 37km,
4) 18:30, 5) 810g, 6) 50 seconds, 7) 86,
8) 21 minutes, 9) 12, 10) 9.

Activity sheet 54 1) £3.29, 2) 1675g, 3) 5,
4) 74, 75, 76, 5) 96 minutes, 6) 134cm, 7) 372,
8) 1600, 9) 8·5kg, 10) 26.

Activity sheet 55 1) 32 499 miles, 2) 86, 87, 88,
3) £37.90, 4) 60cm, 5) 8·2 litres, 6) 46cm, 7) 226,
8) 1383, 9) 119cm, 10) 736.

Solving problems: division

Activity sheet 56 1) 8, 2) 6, 3) 9, 4) 7, 5) 5, 6) 16,
7) 14, 8) 13, 9) 16, 10) 29.

Activity sheet 57 1) 24, 2) 6, 3) 8, 4) 7, 5) 10,
6) 13, 7) 14, 8) 7, 9) 18, 10) 21.

Activity sheet 58 1) 8, 2) 13, 3) 12, 4) 3, 5) 11,
6) 19, 7) 15, 8) 19, 9) 19, 10) 17.

Activity sheet 59 1) 5, 2) 16, 3) 4, 4) 5, 5) 9, 6) 7,
7) 16, 8) 8, 9) 8, 10) 11.

Activity sheet 60 1) 6, 2) 5, 3) 5, 4) 4, 5) 7, 6) 12,
7) 8, 8) 60, 9) 9, 10) 14.

Extracting information: money

Activity sheet 61 1) Eachway, 2) £35.99,
3) Eachway, 4) £25.97, 5) £24.52, 6) £77, 7) £18,
8) £2.

Activity sheet 62 1) Leisure, 2) £6.50, 3) Jolly's,
4) £4.48, 5) £3.51, 6) £17.97, 7) £3, 8) £1.48.

Activity sheet 63 1) Salter's, 2) £54.49,
3) Salter's, 4) £64.48, 5) £53.02, 6) £261.96,
7) £52.65, 8) £12.02.

Activity sheet 64 1) £110.40, 2) £365.80,
3) £300.80, 4) £190.40, 5) £73.80, 6) 271, 7) 36p,
8) £12.06.

Activity sheet 65 1) £8.40, 2) £46.70, 3) £74.20,
4) £58.80, 5) £10.80, 6) 21, 7) 70p, 8) £1.44.

Extracting information: length

Activity sheet 66 1) 20cm, 2) 0·3m, 3) 70cm,
4) 140cm, 5) 1·5m, 6) 10, 7) 1200cm², 8) 32.

Activity sheet 67 1) 30cm, 2) 0·25m, 3) 160cm,
4) 82cm, 5) 2·8m, 6) 7, 7) 600cm², 8) No.

Activity sheet 68 1) 25cm, 2) 25cm, 3) 60cm,
4) 110cm, 5) 2·25m, 6) 5, 7) 750cm², 8) 40.

Activity sheet 69 1) 20cm, 2) 90cm, 3) 324cm²,
4) £14.85, 5) 4·5m, 6) 18, 14, £630, 7) 60.

Activity sheet 70 1) 20cm, 2) 100cm, 3) 625cm²,
4) £44.55, 5) 4·5m, 6) 16, 10, £352, 7) 50.

Extracting information: mass

Activity sheet 71 1) 16–18kg, 2) 45kg, 3) 2kg,
4) 12·5kg, 5) 4, 6) 21·65kg, 7) £10, 8) 500g.

Activity sheet 72 1) 67–69kg, 2) 65kg,
3) 22–23kg, 4) 4kg, 5) 10, 6) 21·25kg, 7) £17,
8) 1·25kg

Activity sheet 73 1) 27–29kg, 2) 75kg, 3) 3kg,
4) 11–12kg, 5) 12, 6) 32·1kg, 7) £9, 8) 1·5kg.

Activity sheet 74 1) 100g, 2) 600g, 3) 960g,
4) 200g, 5) 3, 6) 4, 7) 15g, 8) 360g, 450g, 270g,
540g, 900ml.

Activity sheet 75 1) 175g, 2) 300g, 3) 1·85kg,
4) 575g, 5) 13, 6) 5, 7) 75g, 8) 750g, 375g, 375g.

Extracting information: capacity

Activity sheet 76 1) 1·5 litres, 2) 5, 3) 225ml,
4) 27·5 litres, 5) 100 litres, 6) 4·6 litres, 7) 4·5
litres, 8) 150ml.

Activity sheet 77 1) 12, 2) 1·6 litres, 3) 160ml,
4) 245 litres, 5) 18 litres, 6) 3·7 litres, 7) 320ml,
8) 16 litres.

Activity sheet 78 1) 2·7 litres, 2) 9, 3) 140ml,
4) 39 litres, 5) 175 litres, 6) 5·3 litres,
7) 6·3 litres, 8) 150ml.

Activity sheet 79 1) 98p, 2) 500ml, 3) 1·05 litres,
4) 150ml, 5) 70ml, 6) £3.53, 7) 2 large colas,
8) 35.

Activity sheet 80 1) £1.30, 2) 750ml, 3) 1·6 litres,
4) 450ml, 5) 120ml, 6) £3.21, 7) 4 small colas,
8) 26.

Extracting information: time

Activity sheet 81 1) 8.30 a.m., 2) 2 p.m.,
3) 6 p.m., 4) Yes, 5) 5.30 p.m., 6) 35 minutes,
7) 2h 15min, 8) 22 hours.

Activity sheet 82 1) 08:00, 2) 08:30, 3) 18:30,
4) Yes, 5) 13:00, 6) 18:15, 7) 1h 40min,
8) 7 hours.

Activity sheet 83 1) 08:00, 2) 07:30, 3) 18:30, 4) No, 5) 35 minutes, 6) 19:10, 7) 1h 50min, 8) 25 hours.

Activity sheet 84 1) 7 and a half hours, 2) Saturday, 3) 50 minutes, 4) 3h 20min, 5) 10.13 a.m., 6) 52·2 seconds, 7) 71 seconds, 8) 70 minutes.

Activity sheet 85 1) 10 and a half hours, 2) Thursday, 3) 65 minutes, 4) 3h 30min, 5) 5.49 p.m., 6) 28·8 seconds, 7) 73 seconds, 8) 42 minutes.

Extracting information: number

Activity sheet 86 1) 17, 2) 6, 3) 9, 4) 7, 5) 34, 6) £126, 7) £7.65, 8) 180.

Activity sheet 87 1) 14, 2) 4, 3) 14, 4) 9, 5) 56, 6) £4.14, 7) 24p, 8) 312.

Activity sheet 88 1) 13, 2) 7, 3) 7, 4) 5, 5) 54, 6) £3990, 7) £48.55, 8) 18.

Activity sheet 89 1) 151–160, 2) 2nd and 5th, 3) 800, 4) £487.50, 5) 31–32, 6) 54, 7) 21:35, 8) 14.

Activity sheet 90 1) 66–69, 2) 1st and 4th, 3) 365–380, 4) £238.50, 5) 12, 6) 39, 7) 20:05, 8) 26.

Mental arithmetic: practice test

1) 730, 2) 1500, 3) 8, 4) 50%, 5) 3004, 6) 5500g, 7) 42, 8) 16:45, 9) 36cm^2, 10) 7.10 p.m., 11) 12, 12) 3°C, 13) 340, 14) £20, 15) 55–65, 16) parallelogram, 17) 69, 18) 60, 19) 420, 20) £12, 21) 15, 22) 60, 23) 8, 24) 8, 25) 19cm.

Test questions: no calculator

Test 1

1) 77, 69, 53, 189, 2) 182mm, 3) £2.46, £3.36, 4) Sport, 1h 45min, 1h 5m, 5) 9, 17, 7, 84, 6) 23, 7) 78, 8) 543, 9) 187, 83, 10) 2·65kg or 2650g.

Test 2

1) 9, 56, 24, 102, 2) 148, 27, 6, 3) 15, 4) £13.34, £1.03, £30.80, 5) 152, 232, 174, 197, 6) 375, 7) £370, £580, £180, 8) 775ml, No.

Test questions: calculator allowed

Test 1

1) numbers total 760, many possible answers, 18 and 15, 15 and 21, 2) £293.80, 3) £28.50, 4) 1·35kg, 5, 105g, 5) 40 702, 6) 12, 7) 20, 8) 15, £8007.87, 3.

Test 2

1) 140, 420, 5, 8, 2) £46.74, 3) 87 319, 4) 69, 12, 85p, 5) 3, 6) 14:50, 34 minutes, 16:03, 7) 18, 8) £28.70, 9) B, £19.50, 10) £23.87, £5.29.